M000049949

POTTERY & PORCELAIN

ANTIQUES ROADSHOW

POCKET GUIDE

POTTERY & PORCELAIN

DAVID BATTIE

BBC BOOKS

A MARSHALL EDITION

Published by BBC Books, a division of BBC Enterprises Ltd,
Woodlands, 80 Wood Lane, London W12 0TT

Conceived, edited and designed by
Marshall Editions
170 Piccadilly, London W1V 9DD

ISBN 0 563 37128 5

10 9 8 7 6 5 4 3 2 1

EDITORS GWEN RIGBY, HEATHER MAGRILL
ART EDITOR HELEN SPENCER
PICTURE EDITOR ELIZABETH LOVING
ASSISTANT EDITOR SIMON BEECROFT
ART DIRECTOR JOHN BIGG

ILLUSTRATIONS by János Márffy,
Stan North, Coral Mula
ALL PHOTOGRAPHS by Clive Corless,
except for the following:
CHRISTIE'S IMAGES: 1; 6; 10*b*; 11*t* & *b*;
32*tl*; 38; 39; 50*b*; 52. SPODE: 8*b*; 9*t*.
t = top, *l* = left, *b* = bottom

Valuation is an imprecise art and prices vary for many reasons. The valuations given are estimated auction prices at the time of going to press. As auctions take place in the public arena, this is considered to be the fairest value.

Origination by Master Image, Singapore
Type film by Dorchester Typesetting
Printed and bound in Portugal by Printer Portuguesa

Contents

Introduction

The collector of ceramics, like almost any collector, has to set limits, often arbitrary, on what to buy. With several thousands of years of production worldwide, the range of objects from which to choose is greater than in any other field. Identifying what one is holding in an antiques market may not be easy: on a modern piece most of what one needs to know may be stamped on the back. On an older piece one may only be sure that what one is holding is a plate. For that reason, this book has been arranged by class of object.

Most ceramics – that is, wares made of clay and fired – were for practical use. Some were apparently made as such but, as in China during the Song Dynasty (960–1279), were actually for burial with the dead for use in the afterlife. Even vases, which seem to serve no function but display, may have served as urns for ashes in Roman times or as prizes at the Greek games. Some of these ancient wares, surprisingly perhaps, are not beyond the pocket of the ordinary collector; for instance, a Roman terracotta lamp, 2,000 years old, may cost under £100. The problem is that the cheaper forms run out quickly and then there is a sudden jump in price to thousands of pounds.

But from only the last 200 years of ceramic history in Europe, the collector has an almost limitless choice of form, material, country, factory or artist at prices from a few pence to over £1,000,000. Objects are gradually shuffled along the conveyor belt of time, starting as a cheap teacup at one end and ending as the Holy Grail at the other. With the change in attention goes a rise in price.

It is no coincidence that this little book is largely given over to tablewares – tea, coffee and dinner services. More of these exist than anything else and more are collected than anything else. Collectors like to impose some logic on a frantic world and as a rule want their collections to follow a theme, hence the recent popularity of coffee cans. Coffee cans have straight sides and are more or less the same size – perfect for collecting. Teacups vary enormously and are a quarter the price of a can from the same service. What is more, the teacup *must* have a saucer, the can need not.

Tea has held a special place in English society for 300 years and the vast range of tea wares reflects this. Tea wares and mugs are suitable vehicles to record the British affection both for its monarchy and for other more transitory events, and such commemorative wares have survived in large numbers.

The market at present has a distinct dislike of damage: the minutest chip or hairline crack will put off most buyers, and the price of a damaged item will be, perhaps, a tenth of that of a perfect piece. But for the true collector, who would rather have something damaged than not at all, trading up when a good example comes along, times have never been better. It must be said, however, that the damaged piece will never have the investment potential of a perfect one. One should, however, be buying for pleasure, not for investment.

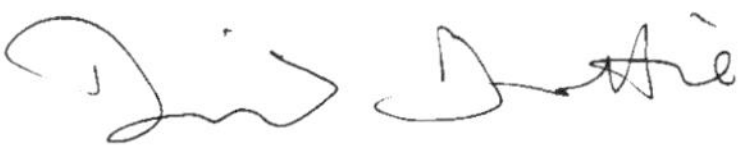

The History of Ceramics

Although the history of ceramics appears complex, there are several broad patterns that run through it.

During prehistoric times, it was discovered that clay could be fixed in a shape by drying it in the sun and, presumably by accident, that fire could create a more lasting effect. At that time, the potter's art was born. Over the centuries, techniques were developed for shaping clay and for refining the clay body, which developed from the basic, porous earthenware to the more robust stoneware that was watertight when fired.

The discovery and development of glaze was another major advance. Not only did a clear glaze seal and enhance the colour of the underlying body, but it could itself be coloured by adding a metallic oxide, resulting in an almost infinite variety of glaze colours and textures.

Developments occurred in many places at different times due to local evolution, conquest or trade. No culture was more prolific than that of China where the advent of the potter's wheel in the 2nd millennium BC revolutionized pottery and led to the refinement of clays necessary for throwing.

Many centuries later, during the Tang Dynasty (618–907)

△ *Imitation-Meissen porcelain plat*

stoneware was refined into the white translucent body known as porcelain or china. It was to take a further thousand years and hundreds of experiments in soft-paste, or artificial, porcelain before Europeans were able to produce their own hard-paste, or true, body.

△ *Salt-glazed stoneware cup.*

It was the growing awareness of Chinese porcelain in the 1300s to 1600s that gave impetus to porcelain-inspired alternative traditions both in Renaissance Europe and in Islamic lands. The use of tin glaze – clear lead glaze with added tin ashes – turned buff-coloured pottery white. This allowed it to be painted and gave rise to some of the most popular European pottery.

△ *Early tin-glazed earthenware (maiolica) wet-drug jars.*

This tin-glazed earthenware flourished in the 1300s and 1400s in Spain, where it was known as Hispano-Moresque, and in Italy, where it was called maiolica. Over time, migrants spread the tradition northward. As production was started in different countries the name of the wares evolved: delftware in England; Delft in the Low Countries; faience in France; and *fayencen* in Germany and Scandinavia.

Once trade with the Far East was under way, the arrival of Chinese and Japanese blue and white porcelain had far-reaching effects on the European earthenware and stoneware industries. It inspired the search for hard-paste porcelain and the refining of more traditional bodies, and led to much artistic imitation of both blue and white wares and colourful Japanese designs.

Around the same time, the formula for true porcelain was discovered and exploited at the Meissen factory near Dresden. For 40 years, only Meissen, and the Du Paquier factory in Vienna, produced hard-paste porcelain. But by the 1750s, Meissen's shapes and decoration were widely imitated in Europe.

It was an earthenware potter, Josiah Wedgwood, who brought the Industrial Revolution to ceramics when he set up his Staffordshire factory in 1759. He improved clay bodies and firing techniques; set up production lines; and used modern marketing techniques.

In the late 18th century, three developments – transfer printing; slip casting; and the creation of the hybrid "bone china" – gave English potters an edge. Allied to the political decline of China in the 1790s, they gave the European industry, especially in England, trading supremacy.

△ *Lead-glazed slipware tyg, or cup.*

Bodies & Glazes

All pottery and porcelain is made from clay which has been hardened by fire. In most instances, the clay has also been refined to create a "body", or paste, with particular qualities of colour and plasticity.

Learning to recognize the material used is the first stage in identifying and dating ceramics; hence the importance of examining the bottom, or foot, of an object where the unglazed clay can be seen.

There are two basic bodies: porous earthenware, which is fired to 900°F–1,500°F; and non-porous stoneware and porcelain, fired to *c*.2,400°F. Porcelain, also called china, can be distinguished from stoneware by its translucency and whiteness. It is divided into two types, soft-paste, or artificial, porcelain and hard-paste, or true, porcelain, which originated in China.

The term "bone china" refers to a special type of soft-paste porcelain to which bone ash has been added. Developed in the late 1700s in Staffordshire, it had been adopted by most English factories by the early 1800s.

△ *A Wedgwood pot being thrown*

The next most important constituent of a piece is the glaze. By applying a glaze, a potter modifies or covers the body. A clear lead glaze, for instance, will convert the buff colour of Staffordshire slipware to a honey tone. An opaque tin glaze covers the body in a white "skin" which can then be painted. Being able to recognize types of glaze is important in identifying a ceramic piece.

The decoration of a piece follows the body and glaze in importance. Lead glaze lends itself to in-glaze colour stains, such as those used on the

△ *Transfer printing Spode's Italian pattern.*

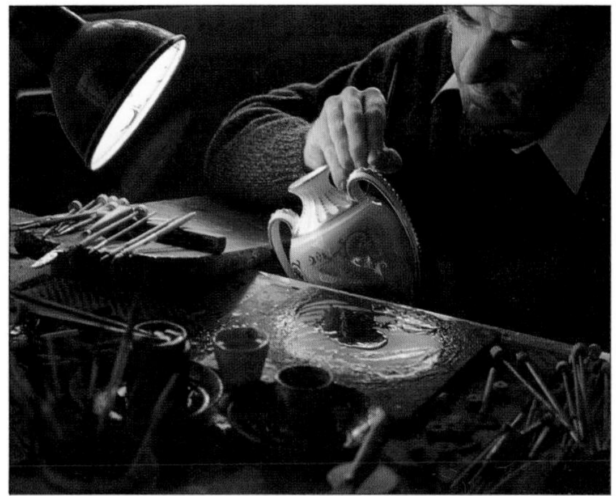

△ *Gilding: the final stage of ornamentation.*

Staffordshire vegetable moulded wares of the 1700s. Monochrome glazes, including browns, reds, blues and spectacular yellows, were perfected by the Chinese. Porcelain glazes are often transparent and colourless to show off the whiteness of the body and give it a sparkle.

In the 1300s, the Chinese found that cobalt blue painted on a piece before it was glazed matured to a strong blue colour when fired. Such metallic oxides, applied and fired under the glaze, are known as underglaze pigments. This discovery was widely copied in both earthenwares and porcelains, all of which are known as blue and white or underglaze blue wares.

Other decoration could be painted or enamelled on top of the glaze. Ceramics may be hand painted or decorated with mass-produced transfer prints; some are even gilded.

Valuable clues for identifying pottery or porcelain can also be derived from the construction method and from the presence of moulded decoration. Neolithic pots were made by building up coils of clay or fixing slabs together. Later came the potter's wheel and throwing followed, later still, by slip casting. The inside of a piece is more likely to divulge the construction method than the finely finished outside.

Moulded decoration can be cut out, impressed, scored or stuck on. Classical friezes were applied to Wedgwood pieces whereas imitations are often part of an all-in-one slip mould.

△ *Cleaning up applied motifs.*

Tea & Coffee Wares

Since the mid-17th century, when tea arrived in the West from China and began to be drunk in coffee houses and later at home, tea and coffee wares made in a wide variety of styles have been among the most popular ceramics. For collectors, the appeal of tea and coffee wares lies in their almost infinite variety: of form, decoration, material, country of origin and style. What is more, prices range from a few pounds to thousands. The growing trend toward collecting one particular shape – teapots or coffee cans for example – means that most services are broken up and the pieces sold individually. The wide range of damaged pieces is an invaluable storehouse for the tyro collector. A cracked tea bowl, for instance, bought for just a nominal amount, can prove the perfect learning tool. Buying damaged and upgrading is an old-established and sensible procedure.

JUGS

It is little wonder that jugs are some of the most common antique ceramics, for they were among the most used domestic items. Milk was measured from the churn into a jug on the doorstep; water was collected from the well or pump in a bucket and ladled out with a jug; and even in the early 1900s, beer and cider were usually fetched from the pub in a jug.

In Britain, early jugs were mainly earthenware; later, stoneware and parian, both of which can be easily moulded, predominated. Jugs are of particular interest to collectors, since they often bear dates, makers' and Registration of Design marks.

△ **STONEWARE JUG** *with stamped and incised decoration typical of the Westerwald region of Germany; the silver mount is a 19th-century addition. c.1690.* **£3,000–£5,000**

△ **ENGLISH CREAMWARE JUG,** *thought to have been made in Newcastle or Sunderland, since it carries the inscription "John & Ann Fletcher Hexham", who were probably a local couple. It would have been used for milk or ale. 1792; 9in high.* **£750–£1,000**

◁ **ENGLISH JUG** *with a traditional fox-hunting scene moulded on the stoneware body, and the neck and handle covered in a vibrant blue enamel. It was made in Staffordshire by Turners, but many other factories produced similar wares. Early 1800s; 9in high.* **£70–£100**

◁ **TURNER'S STONEWARE JUG,** *with the handle and spout in the form of a snake. It may have been meant for wine, since the fine white body is sprigged with a border of fruiting vines, trees and figures of horsemen standing outside an inn. 1810–15; 7½in high.* **£100**

> **BONE-CHINA JUG,** *moulded ɔith daisies, which was used for emonade: the strainer at the base f the spout would have trapped he pips. Jugs of this type were nass produced in Staffordshire; his one was made by Graingers in Vorcester. 1840; 8in high.* **£60–£90**

◁ **MOCHAWARE JUG** *This large jug, which was used to carry beer from the cellar of an inn to the bar, has a second handle beneath the spout. The words read: "The population of Kent in the year 1841 was 54861". The jug would be worth more if it were not slightly damaged. 9½in high.* **£200–£500**

> **SCOTTISH STONEWARE JUG,** *ɔhich is unusual in that it is lecorated with pictures of giraffes n lustre. It was made in Glasgow s a wedding gift and is owned y a direct descendant of the narriage partners. 1875; in high.* **£75–£100**

Mugs

The term mug describes a drinking cup with a single handle and a rim without a lip. It is smaller than a tankard and generally does not have a lid.

Mugs were first made in England in the 16th century and soon took the place of beakers. Eventually, as well as earthenware and stoneware examples for everyday use, fine china mugs, painted with scenes and flowers and often also gilded, were produced by all the major factories.

△ **Derby mug** *of characteristic shape, with ribs at the top and bottom and a fine painting of birds in fresh colours on a very white body. Typical spin marks from the wheel can be seen under the base. Its present owner bought it many years ago for £3.10s, which was then his weekly wage; it has proved a good investment. c.1757; 6in high.* **£1,750**

△ **Worcester mug** *painted in two shades of cobalt blue with a rare design (now known as "The Gardener") showing a Chinese man, a vase of flowers on a table and a kneeling boy at the side. 1765–70; 5in high.* **£700–£1,200**

▷ **Famille-rose mug** *Export wares from China were popular in 18th-century Europe. This attractive mug has intertwined handles and delicate floral decoration in the soft coloration typical of* famille-rose *pieces. c.1785; 8in high.* **£500**

◁ **PEARLWARE MUG,** *probably from a Welsh factory, with a transfer-printed and hand-enamelled steeplechasing design. The name "pearlware" derives from the bluish glaze. The piece is also heavily stained where liquids have penetrated the crazed glaze. 1830s; 3½in high.* **£25–£35**

▷ **ROCKINGHAM MUG** *made in the pottery set up c.1745 by the Earl of Rockingham on his Yorkshire estate. In 1826–47 it also made porcelain pieces, such as this mug depicting the London to York mailcoach, which features Rococo gilded decoration typical of the factory. c.1835; 5in high.* **£1,000**

JOKE LOVING CUP

Frog cups and mugs, such as this ironstone one, have been surprising unwary drinkers since the 1600s. A name and date appear on the mug, so it may have been a christening gift. 1850; 5½in high. **£300**

▷ **CIDER MUG** *in Sunderland lustre. Despite the name, such wares were also made in Liverpool, Bristol and Staffordshire. Purple lustre laid over the glaze was sprayed with oil blown through a muslin-covered tube. In the kiln, the oil expanded and formed bubbles which burst, producing characteristic irregular blotches. c.1860; 3½in high.* **£120**

Commemorative Jugs & Mugs

Events of historic importance, whether they be the death or coronation of a monarch, the first ascent in a balloon or landing of a flying boat, have long been marked by the production of ceramic mementos.

Delftware items were produced in the 17th century to celebrate the restoration of Charles II; Queen Anne was honoured in the same way; and most British rulers since have been similarly commemorated.

In the early 1800s, potters made slip-cast jugs relating to the Napoleonic Wars. Politics and sport, too, were exciting subjects, and the deeds of famous men, from William Gladstone and Winston Churchill to pugilists, are marked on jugs and mugs.

◁▷ **Staffordshire jug** *A rare piece that commemorates the death of the much disliked King George IV. The portrait is very flattering: he weighed 20 stone and is said to have had a spherical body. Where the glaze is thin, the pottery is discoloured, which reduces the jug's value. 1830; 5in high.* **£140**

△ *The base of the jug bears the initials W B for William Brownfield's factory and the registration code for 1863.*

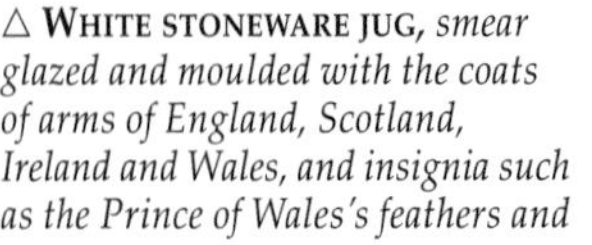

△ **White stoneware jug,** *smear glazed and moulded with the coats of arms of England, Scotland, Ireland and Wales, and insignia such as the Prince of Wales's feathers and Victoria's cypher. It was made in Staffordshire to mark the marriage of Albert Edward, later Edward VII, to Princess Alexandra of Denmark in 1863. 6½in high.* **£80–£120**

DOULTON JUGS

As these stoneware jugs from Doulton's Lambeth factory show, political and sporting figures, such as Disraeli (*left*) and the cricketer W.G. Grace (*below*), were popular subjects for commemorative wares.

△▷ *Jug with moulded and incised decoration, honouring Benjamin Disraeli (above), 1881; 8in high.* **£100–£150**. *Printed cricketers jug (right), 1890s; 7½in high.* **£200–£300**

▽ **PEACE MUG** *produced by the thousand at the end of World War I. The elaborate lithographic transfer print shows the commanders-in-chief of the British sea and land forces. 1919; 4in high.* **£18–£20**

△ **VICTORIAN DIAMOND JUBILEE MUG** *with a white sprigged portrait that has been moulded separately and attached to the blue body. 1897; 3½in high.* **£30–£40**

◁ **CHINA MUG** *for George VI's coronation. There was less time to make items for this event, so this is rarer than mugs for Edward VIII, who abdicated. 1937.* **£10–£20**

TEAPOTS

Tea was first drunk for pleasure in ancient China at the time of the Han Dynasty (206–220 BC); until then its uses had been purely medicinal. Tea was initially made in bowls, but pots were introduced in the Song Dynasty (AD 970–1279), and both tea and teapots began to arrive in the West in the 1650s.

The new beverage rapidly became popular and was made in small teapots because tea cost the equivalent of £800 per pound today.

In the late 17th century, China began to export *famille-verte* biscuit porcelain teapots and Imari designs copied from Japan. Though *famille-rose* ware became popular in Britain in the 1740s, demand was greater for the cheaper blue and white teapots, many of which have survived.

▷ **SALT-GLAZE STONEWARE TEAPOT** *by Wedgwood in the form of a Georgian town house. Salt glaze was popular for English tableware, but owing to dangers in the manufacturing process, the factory ceased production in the late 1700s. c.1750; 6in high.* **£1,500**

◁ **MEISSEN ROSE TEAPOT** *The design of this rare piece is based on a Chinese* blanc de Chine *original; the moulding represents a white rose, with buds for the teapot's feet. Most Meissen flower-encrusted wares date from the 1770s. 1740; 5in high.* **£1,000**

THE CHANGING SHAPE OF THE TEAPOT

CHINESE EXPORT PORCELAIN, 1728

CHELSEA PORCELAIN, MOULDED, 1748

WHIELDON REDWARE, 1750

WORCESTER PORCELAIN, 177

▷ **"FIRST PERIOD" WORCESTER TEAPOT** *based on a contemporary Chinese* famille-rose *original and painted in enamels and gilding. Worcester pieces made before 1780 used to be called "Dr Wall" after one of the original partners; they are now know as "First Period". 1765; 6½in high.* **£600–£900**

◁△ **UNDERGLAZE BLUE TEAPOT** *in Neo-classical shape. One side displays a house in a park, the other a lady named Sally Sikes. Dated 1781; 5½in high.* **£600–£900**

▷ **CREAMWARE TEAPOT** *painted with a stylized plant design on one side and an inscription on the other. Such messages often appear on gifts that sailors gave to their loved ones before setting sail. The feathery decoration and the scroll handle are Rococo features. 1780; 5in high.* **£300–£500**

NEW HALL PORCELAIN, 1790

WEDGWOOD WHITE STONEWARE, 1820

ROCKINGHAM BONE CHINA, 1830–35

COPELAND EARTHENWARE, 1880

Early 18th-century teapots were globular or pear shaped, but in the 1740s and '50s, during the Rococo period, there was a vogue for eccentric teapots shaped like shells, camels, houses and even fat "Chinamen".

In the mid-18th century the inspiration for many English and French styles was provided by early Chinese teapots, such as those made from Yixing ware (a red stoneware body which supposedly produced the best tea) and *blanc de Chine*, from southeast China.

The 19th century saw a return to globular teapots; Wedgwood's black basalt, "squashed" disc-shaped pots were particularly striking. The Eastern influence produced unusual styles such as bamboo-effect pots, while the Rococo revival in the 1830s resulted in elaborate flower-encrusted pots. Most bizarre, however, were animal-shaped pots that appeared with the advent of majolica in the 1860s.

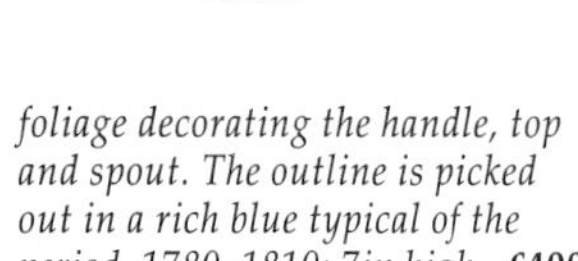

▷ **BLACK BASALT TEAPOT** *in a style associated with Wedgwood, although this example is made by an unknown copyist. Few people collect basalt unless it is marked Wedgwood – possibly because of its sombre colour. The figure on the cover is the biblical Widow of Zaraphath. 1790s; 5in high.* **£100**

▽ **WHITE STONEWARE TEAPOT** *made by Clulow and Co. in Fenton, Staffordshire. The overall design shows a strong Classical influence. The moulded details include a figure standing beside an urn and foliage decorating the handle, top and spout. The outline is picked out in a rich blue typical of the period. 1780–1810; 7in high.* **£400**

◁ **EARTHENWARE TEAPOT** *made by Harley of Lane End and coloured in the "Pratt" palette under a pearlware glaze. It is unstained, which is rare, but the castellation and the swan's head are damaged; in perfect condition the value could be four times as much. 1805; 4in high.* **£100**

▷ **REGENCY TEAPOT** *The brightly coloured enamels and gilding used to decorate this well-made piece are typical of many Regency wares. Although its shape follows that of classic silver Regency teapots, there is basketry-style moulding on the sides. 1810–20; 7in high.* **£1,200–£1,600**

CADOGAN TEAPOT

This teapot style developed from the Chinese peach-shaped wine pot supposedly first used by Lady Cadogan in the late 18th century. It works on the unspillable inkwell principle and is filled through a hole in the underside, with an inner tube that runs to just below the top. This Spode example is rare; pieces by Rockingham are more usual. 1820; 8in high. **£250**

▷ **STAFFORDSHIRE TEAPOT** *made of white stoneware. The cast is of good quality, and the decorative pattern includes stylized palmettes on a seeded ground. Victorian pottery such as this can often be found quite inexpensively. c.1865; 5in high.* **£60**

▽ **MINTON MAJOLICA TEAPOT** *in the shape of a monkey clutching a coconut. The spout is chipped, but otherwise this is an excellent example of the japonaiserie made following the London Exhibition of 1867. The design of the monkey's jacket imitates an embroidered Japanese jacket. 1870; 5in high.* **£700**

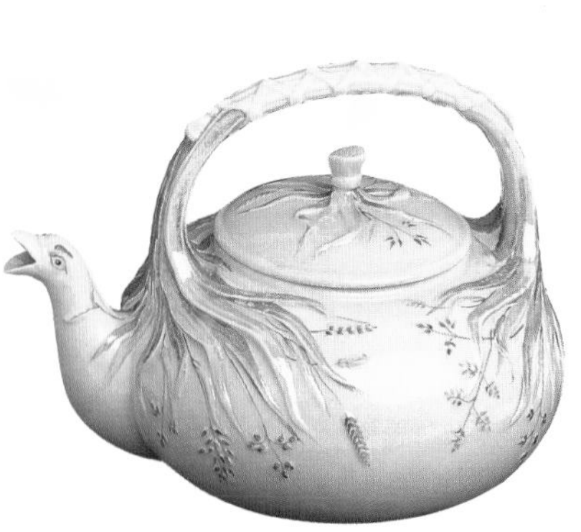

◁ **BELLEEK TEA KETTLE** *The design of this piece, called "Grass", is picked out in enamels and lustrous pink. The Belleek factory in County Fermanagh, Northern Ireland, made both tea kettles – which have overhead handles, as here – and teapots with side handles. 1880; 7in high.* **£300**

◁ **HEXAGONAL TEAPOT** *made in Staffordshire of earthenware with restrained blue and black decoration. In the late 19th century, teapots were largely mass produced in almost infinite variety. Despite this, the sheer range of designs makes this a rich period for collectors. Late 19th century; 8in high.* **£25–£35**

▷ **JAPANESE TEAPOT** *This form of pot, made in Seto, has two loops to take a basketwork handle. These pots were made in great numbers and are therefore very inexpensive. c.1920; 3in high.* **£2–£10**

A MEASHAM "BARGE TEAPOT"

This large dated teapot, made in Measham, Derbyshire, has an unusual double spout and a lid in the shape of a tiny teapot. The nickname "barge teapot" originated in the late 19th century, when such pots were owned by bargees in the Staffordshire area. These workers often spent their holidays picking hops and, if money was tight, they walked, taking the teapot with them, instead of catching a train. 1895; 11in high. **£100**

Tea Services

The first tea bowls, saucers and teapots arrived in the West with the first shipments of tea from China. From the mid-18th century, matched porcelain tea sets based on Oriental designs were being produced by continental makers. Full sets comprised a teapot, teapot stand, sugar box and cover, milk jug (sometimes with a lid), slop bowl, bread plates, spoon tray, tea and coffee cups and saucers.

Some of the earliest European tea wares were produced by Meissen, in Saxony, first in a hard red stoneware, and later in white hard-paste porcelain. From the 1740s, finely painted Rococo sets appeared, with some of the finest examples made by the French factory, Sèvres.

In England, from the mid-1740s, tea services were made in soft-paste porcelain by Chelsea, and in the 1760s Wedgwood developed a cream-coloured earthenware he called Queen's Ware, which was popular throughout Europe.

△ **Hand-painted tea service** *by Minton, whose early bone-china tablewares rivalled those of other makers such as Spode, Mason and Davenport. This virtually complete set, with botanical decoration, is Minton at its best: each piece carries the famous crossed L mark, with M and the pattern number, here 786 (inset). 1812;* Cups *2½in high.* The set **£1,500–£2,000**

▷ **Coalport tea service** *Any elaborate Rococo-revival tea service was once attributed to Rockingham, but research has now disclosed who made what. Pattern numbers can frequently provide the necessary evidence. c.1830;* Teapot *7in high.* **£1,250**

△ **MEISSEN PART TEA SET** *consisting of tea bowls and saucers and a covered sugar bowl with a floral knop. They are painted with figures in German landscapes, probably near Dresden, where the Meissen factory was situated. 1740;* Tea bowl *1¾in high.* **£2,500**

◁ **PINK LUSTRE TEA SERVICE** *by Dawson of Sunderland. Although impressed marks are rarely seen on lustre pottery, this example is marked. The panels of figures are transfer printed and hand coloured. 1821;* Teapot *5in high.* **£450**

Many English tea services imitated Japanese Kakiemon porcelain in iron-red, blue, yellow and turquoise enamels, as well as Imari patterns of alternating bands of decoration.

When bone china was invented in the early 19th century, great numbers of tea services were made using this fine white translucent porcelain; Spode's hand-painted wares are particularly collectable.

Some of the finest late 19th-century sets are enamelled wares made by Royal Worcester and Copeland. Some sets did not include a teapot, sugar bowl or cream jug; these would have been in silver. A set without these pieces today, therefore, is not necessarily incomplete.

Full tea services command the highest prices. Less dear are incomplete sets which, with at least six pieces, are quite usable.

THE CABARET TEA SET

When morning tea was taken in the bedroom, a variation on the full tea service was used – the "cabaret" set. These usually comprised one or two cups and saucers, a teapot, milk jug, sugar bowl and slop bowl, all on a matching tray.

◁ **CABARET, OR "SOLITAIRE", TEA SET** *in underglaze blue and bright enamels on Empire-style forms. The best examples of these sets were made by Swansea; this one, however, is by Coalport or Davenport. 1810–15;* Teapot *5in high.* **£600–£1,000**

▷ **MINTON MAJOLICA TEA SET** *Tea sets of this type are highly sought after, since they rarely survive intact. The pieces are marked with the maker's name, the pattern and mould number, the potter's mark and the date code. Date codes in a set commonly varied by a few years. 1872–74;* Teapot *5in high.* **£3,000**

△ **DOULTON STONEWARE TEA SET** *with moulded decoration. Initially, Doulton specialized in stoneware drainpipes, but produced art wares after 1860. Were this set complete – one cover does not match – it would be worth half as much again. 1879;* Teapot *4in high.* The set **£250**.

△ **"JACOBETHAN"-STYLE TEA SET** *Each of the pieces is slip cast as an oak-beamed cottage in a curious hybrid of the Elizabethan and Jacobean styles in architecture. Such pieces were popular in the early years of the 20th century. c.1920; 2½–4½in high.* **£60–£80**

△ **JAPANESE EGGSHELL SERVICE** *Millions of these sets were exported from c.1900 to c.1939. Most were thinly potted and crudely painted, often within a transfer or stencilled guide, as here. This set was probably made in Kutani. 1920;* Teapot *9in high.* Each piece **£2–£3**

Coffee Services

Before tea became popular, coffee and chocolate were the most common non-alcoholic drinks, both in the home and in the coffee houses which had sprung up all over Europe.

The habit of drinking coffee spread from the Near East, and the first coffee pots looked like Turkish wine jugs, but the shape soon changed to resemble that of the teapot, with a cover and, usually, a handle opposite the spout. Chocolate pots looked much like coffee pots, except for a hole in the lid through which a stick, or *molinet*, was inserted to stir up the contents.

The Meissen Influence

The formula for hard-paste porcelain, first made in Europe at Meissen in 1710, was coveted by all the other makers of ceramics. Although the secret was jealously guarded, artisans at the factory left to work elsewhere, taking their knowledge with them, and within 20 years imitations of Meissen porcelain were being made throughout the Germanic countries, in France and in Britain.

Ludwigsburg coffee pot, *inspired by Meissen. 1760s; 9in.* **£1000–£1,500**

Meissen chocolate pot *with typical ear-shaped handle. 1740s; 8in high.* **£2,000**

▷ **Porcelain coffee set** *in Empire style, with well- painted views and gilding in good condition, probably made in Paris. The set consists of 14 cups, a small coffee pot and a milk jug; originally it there would also have been a covered sugar bowl and plates but not necessarily saucers. c.1820.* Set as it is **£500**

▷ **Milk jug and cover** *of a shape often included in tea and coffee sets and made at Caughley, Shropshire. The factory, set up in 1772 and taken over by Coalport in 1799, made mainly blue and white wares imitating those from Worcester, but also some fine polychrome pieces. This jug was painted and gilded in the London studio of James Giles, the foremost decorator of the day. 1775; 5in high.* **£1,200–£1,500**

▽ **Noritake coffee set** *in eggshell porcelain. It is unusually well decorated in a design based on a Chinese textile. Thousands of these sets were exported by the Japanese, and the extreme thinness of the porcelain has, paradoxically, ensured their survival, since people were afraid to use them. 1920;* Coffee pot *7in high.* **£100**

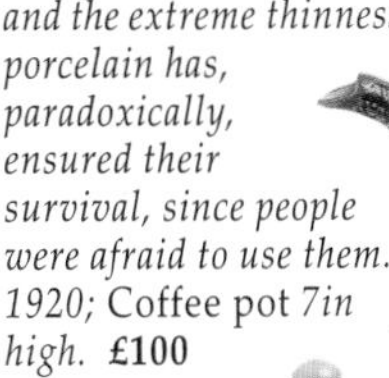

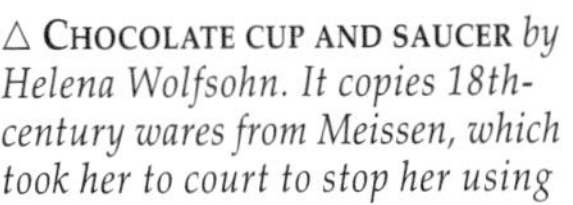

△ **Chocolate cup and saucer** *by Helena Wolfsohn. It copies 18th-century wares from Meissen, which took her to court to stop her using their designs and the AR monogram of Augustus Rex, Elector of Saxony, the founder of the factory. 1880;* Cup *2¾in high.* **£40–£60**

CUPS & SAUCERS

The origins of the tea cup lie in the handleless *chawan,* or tea bowl, used in traditional Buddhist tea ceremonies. European examples were first made, in silver, in the early 1600s, and in ceramics later in the century.

Cups with handles appeared in the 1770s, and the traditional tea-cup shape of a wide, shallow bowl with a handle was established by 1760. Decoration on English cups was frequently a combination of hand painting and transfer-printed patterns, but hand painting continued for both the best and worst wares. On shallow mid-Victorian cups, the decoration was often on the inside, where it was more easily seen, with only a simple gilded motif on the outside.

Tea cups are ideal for collectors on a limited budget, since good-quality items can be found plentifully and inexpensively.

THE TEA BOWL

◁ **JAPANESE CHAWAN,** *or tea bowl, of traditional deep form. The low-fired bricklike body is deep salmon pink and grey. It is signed by the noted maker Ryonyu. Mid-19th century; 3in high.* **£600–£800**

▷ **CHELSEA TEA BOWL AND SAUCER** *Sets are often broken up nowadays and the pieces sold as cups and saucers or as trios. c.1770;* Saucer *4in diameter.* **£80–£120**

◁ **TEA BOWL** *made in Suffolk at the Lowestoft factory. Early examples are in underglaze blue; later pieces employed enamel colouring, particularly red, as here. 1880–85; 1½in high.* **£80**

△ **CUP, TEA BOWL AND SAUCER** *This set, referred to as a "trio", is decorated with a black overglaze transfer scene (called "l'Amour") engraved by Robert Hancock, who developed the technique at Worcester. Overglaze is applied on top of the glaze and is thus very prone to wear, which affects the price. 1775;* Saucer *5in.* **£250–£350**

▷ **"FIRST PERIOD" OCTAGONAL TEA CUP** *made by Worcester with a scroll handle and typically restrained use of Kakiemon-style decoration in a* famille-verte *palette. 1753–55; 2¼in high.* **£1,000**

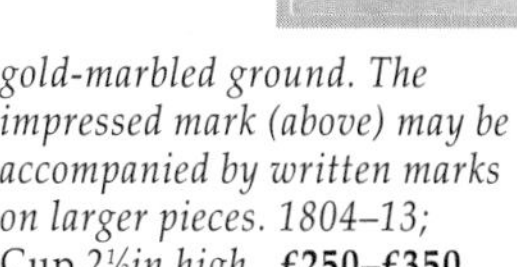

△ **TEA CUP AND SAUCER** *by Barr, Flight & Barr, who worked at Worcester in the Regency period. The pieces are bat printed (a variation of transfer printing which gives the most superior reproduction) in black with Classical subjects on a simulated gold-marbled ground. The impressed mark (above) may be accompanied by written marks on larger pieces. 1804–13;* Cup *2½in high.* **£250–£350**

▷ **TEA CUP AND SAUCER** *made by H. & R. Daniel, with the pattern number 4581. The decoration, of birds on tree branches, at the bottom of the cup (not visible) and the burnished gilding on a deep blue ground, is typical of late Regency wares. The cup is one of 12 belonging to a set now comprising a teapot, 2 plates, 8 coffee cups, 11 saucers, a slop bowl and a milk jug. 1830;* Saucer *4in.* Set **£300–£400;** Cup and saucer **£15–£20**

△ **GIANT STAFFORDSHIRE CUP AND SAUCER,** *transfer-printed with the Chinese-influenced Willow pattern. It has a typically bright and brassy mercury-gilt line border. These cups were not simply ornaments, but were used by factory workers or miners, who often consumed several pints of tea after returning home from a shift. 1880; 4in high.* **£35**

▷ **SHAMROCK-PATTERN TEA CUP** *The Belleek tea service from which this item derives has 12 cups and saucers, teapot, hot water jug, sugar bowl and milk jug. Belleek tea services carry a mark to reassure owners that the extraordinarily thin teapot walls will not crack. The pattern is still made today. 1895;* Saucer *5½in wide.* **£40–£60**

△ **JAPANESE CUP AND SAUCER,** *with a decorative theme of large butterflies on a deep blue ground, made by Noritake for the European market. Cloisonné was frequently similarly decorated, as were pieces from Wedgwood. Early 1900s;* Saucer *5½in.* **£40**

◁ **"LIMPET" DESIGN TEA SET** *Part of a Belleek set that was first made in about 1880 and produced until 1989; this one carries a black "third period" (1926–46) mark. When, as here, they lack the teapot, sets may be bought by dealers, who sell the pieces separately. c.1930;* Plate *12in.* The set **£400**

▷ **ART DECO CUP AND SAUCER** *from a breakfast set for four people, complete with teapot, creamer and sugar bowl. The decoration on this piece follows the Art Deco style prevalent at the time, and, although such sets are relatively inexpensive at the moment, their value is increasing steadily. 1930; 3in high.* **£10–£15**

TABLEWARES

The earliest English soft-paste porcelain dinner services, made from the mid-18th century, are today virtually impossible to find complete. Indeed, single pieces of these tablewares, made only for the wealthy, are still out of the financial reach of the average collector. But once greater numbers of wares were made for an expanding middle class, the choice becomes vast. From the 1760s, creamware dominated the dining table, to be succeeded toward the end of the century by pearlware, also a Josiah Wedgwood development; and early in the 19th century, durable ironstone appeared. As with tea and coffee wares, services are often broken to suit collectors and the important interior decorators' market. As a result, more sought-after pieces, such as a pair of sauce tureens with covers and stands, could fetch up to £1,000, whereas a plate from the same service may make only £30–£50.

Dinner Services

Silver, pewter or wood were commonly used for tablewares in Europe until the 1500s, and such ceramic tablewares as there were consisted of individual bowls or plates, or perhaps a run of several in the same shape and pattern.

Plates and dishes in tin-glazed earthenware, known as Delft in Holland and delftware in England, were made throughout the 17th and 18th centuries, but they chipped easily. Josiah Wedgwood's lead-glazed creamware, which he named Queen's Ware, produced from the mid-18th century, was more satisfactory, but large, elaborate dinner services as such were not made until later in the century.

The grandest of these contained soup and meat plates, dishes in various sizes for meat and fish, vegetable dishes, and tureens for both soup and sauces. Sometimes plates and dishes for dessert were also included.

△ **Chelsea claret-ground part service** *Chelsea porcelain is divided into four periods, indicated by factory marks. An incised triangle (1745–49) was followed until 1752 by an anchor, moulded in relief on a pad. The red anchor marks a period (1752–57) when many of the best-known Chelsea pieces were made. The plates here, with ornate floral designs, rich ground colour and fine gilding inspired by Sèvres wares, are typical of the gold anchor period (1757–69). c.1765;* Plate *12in.* Pair of plates **£800–£1,200**

△ **VIENNA PART DINNER SERVICE**
By bribing Meissen workers to defect to it, the long-lived Vienna factory (1718 to the early 1800s) was the second in Europe to achieve hard-paste porcelain. The similarity to Meissen wares is evident in the painting of the European flowers and in the palette, while the moulding shows a strong Rococo influence. c.1765; Oval dish *15in long.* Pair of dishes **£400–£600**

△ **COALPORT PART DINNER SERVICE**
These items, from a set of more than 100 remaining pieces, are decorated with a bold Japanese pattern in underglaze blue and gilt, with red, yellow and brown flowerheads and trailing honeysuckle. The tureens have gilt lion's head handles and lion finials on the lids. Coalport produced more dinner services than any other factory at this time. c.1810. **£5,000–£7,000**

PLATES & DISHES

The Chinese discovered how to make porcelain in the 7th century, but it was not until the 14th century that they discovered that black cobalt oxide under the glaze turned blue when fired. At first, blue and white pieces were all made for export to the the Middle East, and it was only in the 16th century that quantities of blue and white porcelain, known as "kraak", were sent to Europe.

After the establishment of the Qing Dynasty in 1644, the export of porcelain to the West became a flood. Some of these wares were armorials, dinner

◁ **KRAAK CHARGER** *In the mid-16th century, a style of decoration on Chinese porcelain known as kraak (after the ships, or carracks, in which it was exported) became popular in Europe. All kraak pieces were thinly potted and painted with a central design and a border of flowers, knots and precious objects. c.1600; 19in.* **£2,000–£3,000**

▷ **MEAT DISHES** *from a Chinese export dinner service. Many such platters have survived, and their shape and style were also widely copied. c.1760; 14in, 13in long.* Each **£120**

◁ **CHINESE PLATE** *in underglaze blue and white, enriched in iron-red and gold. The colour was probably added in Europe, a process known as clobbering. Plates like this fetch less than those with only blue decoration. Late 1600s; 9in.* **£100**

services painted in *famille-rose* and *famille-verte* enamels to the order of European families.

Cheaper blue and white wares continued to dominate the market, however, and the palette was copied in Europe, first in the Dutch tin-glazed earthenware known as Delft, and then in the ubiquitously produced English delftware. The popularity of such wares is undiminished today.

△ **Unusual Chinese export plate** *painted in a refined style in underglaze blue, iron-red and other enamels. The curious fan shape may have been a family crest. 1720–40; 10in.* **£300–£500**

△ **Famille-verte dish** *The decoration on this shallow dish, with its predominantly leaf-green colouring, is more to Chinese taste than is usual in export ware. 1700; 13in.* **£1,000–£1,500**

Armorial Wares

In the 1700s, English families sent coats of arms to China to be painted on dinner services, sometimes with amusing mistakes, although the quality of the work was usually high.

△ **The crest** *of the Vernons of Hanbury Hall has here been rendered as a girl with a sheaf of rice. 1730.* **£1,500–£2,000**

△ **Plate** *with the owner's labels wrongly incorporated into the banner beneath the arms. 1740; 8¼in.* **£1,200**

△ **Meat Dish** *in underglaze blue with a crest, the initials "IK" and a motto in English. 1780s; 18in.* **£300–£600**

In contrast to the flourishing trade in ceramics with China, that with Japan was limited, particularly after access was all but closed to the West in the 1630s. Of those wares that did reach Europe, Kakiemon porcelain was the most prized, but its influence never matched that of Chinese wares.

It was not until 1713 that true hard-paste porcelain was made in Europe, at the Meissen factory outside Dresden, and it was some time before the formula was spread by defecting workmen to factories in Vienna and, eventually, France.

Although soft-paste porcelain was produced by many factories in Britain, among the best of which was Chelsea, true hard-paste porcelain, or bone china, was not made until 1780. And several factories, most notably Wedgwood, continued to make superb earthenwares, such as creamware and pearlware.

▷ **RARE KAKIEMON PLATE** *made at Arita in Japan. Kakiemon is one of the most coveted types of Japanese porcelain. It usually had skilfully applied multicoloured translucent enamelling; very little was decorated in blue only. Such plates are worth more sold individually than as part of a set. 1720; 8in.*
£1,500–£2,000

◁ **ENGLISH DELFTWARE PLATE** *made at Wincanton, Somerset. The design shows a lady in a garden, with sponged-on trees in a manganese oxide dye, which produces the dark plum colour. The plate is in fine condition and is most unusual in that it depicts a European scene; most of this type of delftware shows Chinese scenes. c.1745–50; 9in.*
£500–£600

◁ **CHELSEA PLATE** *This fine piece of porcelain from the red anchor period (1752–57) demonstrates the way in which painters created designs to cover up imperfections that frequently occurred during firing, sometimes giving the decoration a slightly haphazard look. Here, the greengage covers a rough patch on the surface and a beetle disguises a firing hole. 8in.* **£700–£1,000**

ROYAL PLATES

Russian royalty were enthusiastic patrons of the great ceramics factories in France, Germany and England, and pieces with royal connections are much sought after today.

△ "**FROG" PLATE** *from a dinner service ordered from Wedgwood by Catherine the Great of Russia for the Grenouillière Palace in St. Petersburg* (grenouille *is the French for frog*)*. 1773–74; 9in.* **£12,000–£15,000**

▽ **SÈVRES PORCELAIN PLATES** *based on Sèvres designs first produced c.1775. They were made for the Russian royal yacht, and one of the plates bears the mark for Nicholas II, 1891, the other the mark for Alexander III, 1903.* Both plates *9½in.* The pair **£3,000**

▷ **WEDGWOOD PEARLWARE PLATE** *Josiah Wedgwood introduced this fine white earthenware in 1779 as a development of his "Queen's Ware", which was itself a refined form of creamware that could be easily potted and decorated. The blue tint of the pearlware glaze made it nearer to the Chinese originals. c.1810; 9in.* **£40**

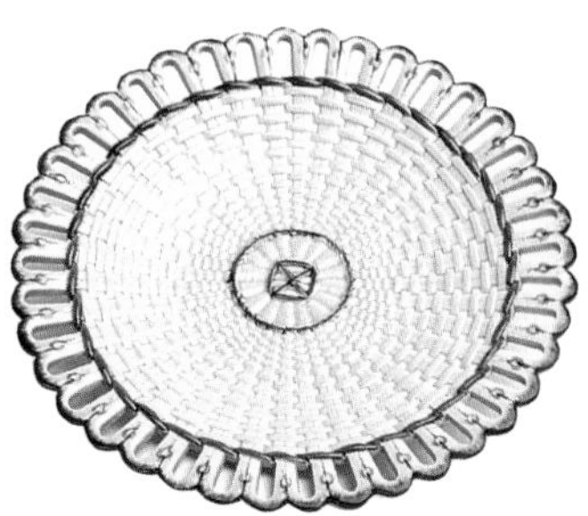

△ **PEARLWARE PLATES,** *two of a set of six which were probably made in Yorkshire and painted with exotic birds by young girls in the factory. Such plates are much sought after by collectors. c.1820; 9½in.* The set **£1,500–£2,000**

WILLOW PATTERN DESIGN

Probably the most famous of all Staffordshire transfer-printed designs, Willow Pattern was inspired by Chinese blue and white ware. This plate, by Dillwyn & Co. of Swansea, includes all the usual features: five stylized trees; a boat; a zigzag fence; a pair of birds and figures on a bridge. 1820–30; 10in. **£50**

CHILDREN'S PLATES

Pottery wares made for children are also becoming popular with collectors. They tended not to last long and it is rare to find them in good condition. These plates, printed with scenes from the biblical story of Joseph, are of better quality than usual. The moulded border is typical of the Swansea Pottery. 1820–30; 6½in. Each **£100**

◁ **MINTON PLATE** *from a dessert service. The tradition of fine painting on bone-china dessert services was maintained in the 1870s by French artists such as Antoine Boullemier. This Sèvres-style scene, within a turquoise border, is typical of his work. 1875; 8in.* **£200–£300**

▷ **PLATE** *decorated with a steam locomotive after the artist and graphic designer Eric Ravilious (1903–42), who produced several such images in a "Travel" series for Wedgwood in the 1930s. Pieces decorated with Ravilious's designs are much sought after. 1936–40; 10in.* **£120**

Commemorative Wares

Makers of ceramics have always been quick to produce special commemorative pieces with an instant appeal to the buying public. As well as mugs and jugs, fine plates have been made, which form a rewarding field for the collector with historical interests.

Among the earliest are the delftware plates commemorating Charles II's restoration to the English throne in 1660, and mementos of royal occasions have remained a constant.

There has also, over the centuries, been a steady flow of plates and bowls marking events of public interest, such as battles, which are highly collectable.

◁ **English delftware plate,** *probably made by the factory at Lambeth in London. This entertaining plate, of interest to devotees of ballooning as well as collectors, commemorates the ascent in 1784 in a hot-air balloon by Vincent Lunardi. 1785; 9in.* **£800–£1,000**

▷ **Scottish pearlware** *porridge bowl inscribed "Waterloo". It was, possibly, made at the Portobello factory in Leith and is extremely rare. c.1815; 5in wide.* **£400–£600**

◁ **Pottery bowl** *made at the Portobello factory almost exactly 100 years later than the bowl above. This patriotic piece, with the words "It's a long way to Tipperary" and showing marching soldiers, crowns and flags, perhaps commemorates the Battle of the Somme. c.1916; 7in across.* **£60–£80**

ROYAL COMMEMORATIVE PLATES

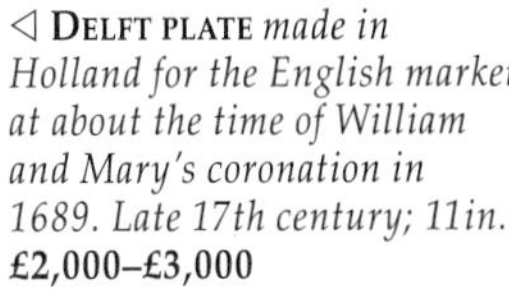

◁ **DELFT PLATE** *made in Holland for the English market at about the time of William and Mary's coronation in 1689. Late 17th century; 11in.* **£2,000–£3,000**

▷ **ENGLISH DELFTWARE CHARGER** *showing William, who reigned alone (1693–1704) after Mary's death. c.1700; 13½in.* **£4,000–£6,000**

◁ **PLATE** *made in support of Queen Caroline after she was locked out of Westminster Abbey during the coronation of George IV. 1820; 3½in.* **£150–£250**

▷ **QUEEN VICTORIA GOLDEN JUBILEE PLATE** *Similar plates were made to celebrate her Diamond Jubilee 10 years later. 1887; 9in.* **£40–£60**

◁ **PARAGON CHINA PLATE** *in a design made for the coronation of Edward VIII and adapted for his brother George VI. 1937; 8in.* **£150–£200**

Bowls

Since the earliest times, bowls have been used for storing, cooking and eating. Bowls were among the grave goods in ancient China, and 18th-century blue and white bowls were among the earliest Chinese ceramics to reach the West.

By the 1700s demand was great for Oriental export pieces, often painted with designs requested by western clients. In Holland and in England, in an attempt to capture some of this trade, earthenware bowls were made that closely followed Oriental styles and decoration, although commemorative themes were also popular.

Because they are difficult to display, bowls are often cheaper than plates: they cannot be wall-mounted, and any interior decoration is hidden if they are used to hold fruit or flowers, say, or pot-pourri.

◁ **Dutch Delft bowl** *painted with Chinese landscape scenes. Delft wares were soft, and pieces were easily damaged, this being no exception: it has a large hairline crack and a chip on the foot, halving its value. 1710; 14in wide.* **£300**

▷ **Dutch tin-glazed earthenware bowl** *English examples may be difficult to distinguish from the Dutch. Although made some 20 years later than the one above, the shape is comparable. 1731; 15in wide.* **£3,000**

◁ **Staffordshire pottery bowl** *transfer printed with a band of roses and a country scene in a rich blue. The subject matter is attractive – scenes showing a rural way of life are popular. c.1840; 9in wide.* Cracked **£30**; In perfect condition **£80**

◁ **CREAMWARE BOWL** *An uncommon piece, probably made in Yorkshire. The surface of the plain earthenware body has been decorated in brown and blue with liquid clay slip which has been "joggled" to resemble agate. c.1780; 7in wide.* **£150–£250**

▷ **SUNDERLAND LUSTRE BOWL** *with transfer prints of the cast-iron bridge over the River Wear (represented on this pottery throughout the 19th century), various nautical rhymes and a picture of the Sailor's Farewell. It has the somewhat hastily decorated look of a middle-period piece. c.1850; 10in wide.* **£300**

◁ **JAPANESE IMARI BOWL** *typically decorated in underglaze blue, iron-red and gilding and, here, with additional green and yellow enamels. The shape of the bowl is typical of wares made for export during the 19th century and into the 20th. 1900; 10in wide.* **£100–£150**

▷ **FRENCH FAIENCE BOWL** *The base of this good-quality decorative bowl, with its brightly enamelled flowers, bears the mark of Le Nove. Production of this type of ware has continued at the factory from the 18th century to the present. 1920s; 14in wide.* **£300–£400**

TUREENS & SAUCEBOATS

In Britain in the 18th century, entertaining among an increasingly large middle class led to the introduction of a wide range of dinner wares. Among them were large covered tureens for soup and vegetables and small tureens and sauceboats – oval boat-shaped dishes on a foot – for sweet and savoury sauces.

The shapes of ceramic pieces followed those of contemporary silver, and porcelain tureens were often equipped with their own stands and many even had accompanying ladles.

Early silver sauceboats had handles at each end and lips on either side, but their porcelain counterparts usually had the handle opposite the lip. Sauceboats generally had a stand and, as with tureens, where this is missing, the value is reduced.

△ **TUREEN, COVER AND STAND** *painted in blue and white with peonies and chrysanthemums. Both the shape and decoration are typical of Chinese wares made expressly for export to European markets during the 18th century. 1750;* Stand *16in wide.* **£1,500–£2,000**

◁ **SAUCEBOAT** *with moulded swags painted in enamels; a rare item from Benjamin Lund's Bristol factory, taken over by Worcester in 1752. c.1751; 8in long.* **£2,00–£3,000**

▷ **RARE PLYMOUTH SAUCEBOAT** *by William Cookworthy, the Quaker chemist who developed the formula for true porcelain in Britain. c.1770; 3in high.* **£500**

△ **SAUCE TUREEN, COVER AND LADLE** *made at Worcester and painted with landscape panels and fruit in a pattern known as "The Lord Henry Thynne" after the eldest son of the then Marquis of Bath. With the stand, the price would be double. c.1775; 5in long.* **£2,500**

◁ **SOUP TUREEN** *in Mason's ironstone. It was transfer printed in greyish black with Imari-style flowers, which were then hand painted. Since enamels and the gilding matured at different temperatures, a piece might be fired several times. c.1820; 7in high.* **£500**

△ **WORCESTER SAUCE TUREEN** *which owes its origins to Sèvres. The overlapping scales and the floral panels are typical of Worcester at this date. There is a pseudo-Chinese mark on the base. c.1770; 9in wide.* **£1,500–£2,000**

Dessert Services

In the mid-18th century, it became fashionable at the end of a meal to have dessert: fruit, nuts, ices, custard and so on. Special dessert services were being produced and, since they did not have to withstand the rough treatment of the meat course, they tended to be the richest and most impressive services of the meal.

Dessert services usually consisted of baskets and dishes for fruit and sweetmeats, bowls, tureens and plates that were a little smaller than dinner plates. The decoration included landscapes, flowers and birds, often with elaborate gilding. Well-painted sets with yellow borders are especially valuable, since the colour was so hard to fire.

△ **Derby dessert service** *The factory at Derby became renowned for high-quality decoration on porcelain. In the late 18th century and early 19th, botanical painting was especially fashionable, with specimen flowers depicted in great detail and in vivid colours. In this dessert service in the style of John Brewer, one of the skilled artists working for the factory, the back of each piece bears both the common and scientific names of the flower. c.1800.* **£35,000–£45,000**

MINTON FRUIT DISH

In 1793, Thomas Minton set up a pottery in Stoke-on-Trent that was to become one of the great names in British ceramics. By the early 19th century, he was making high-quality bone-china tablewares in a wide range of painted, printed and gilded patterns. The design on this dish for fruit and nuts, part of a large dessert service, is loosely based on a design found on ceramics from the Far East. 1805; 10in wide. **£200–£300**

MINTON MARKS

PAINTED, 1800–30

MINTON & HOLLINS, PRINTED, 1845–68

*c.*1850 ONWARD

PRINTED, 1860–69

◁ **CENTRE DISH** *from a dessert service made by W. & R. Ridgway. This maker's wares usually have a solid ground of rather dull grey, but the marbled ground here has been stipple printed (a mass-production technique) in an attempt to copy contemporary hand-painted botanical services. c.1830; 13½in long.* **£250–£300**

▷ **SPODE BAT-PRINTED DISH** *with gilding. Bat printing was a form of transfer printing in which the design was printed in oil on a flexible sheet, or bat, of gelatine and glue. This was pressed into the porcelain and dusted with black powder before firing. 1810–15; 11in long.* **£100**

▽ **BASE MARK FOR 1807–13** *The most technically proficient Worcester porcelain was made from 1792 to 1840, when the factory was controlled by Thomas Flight and the two Martin Barrs (father and son). The marks vary during this period, but always carry the three names.*

△ **WORCESTER DESSERT DISH** *The bold and unusual design on this dish, originally part of a large set, uses Gothic features, such as the stylized oak leaves, within a Japanese Imari-style pattern. 1808; 8in square.* **£100–£150**

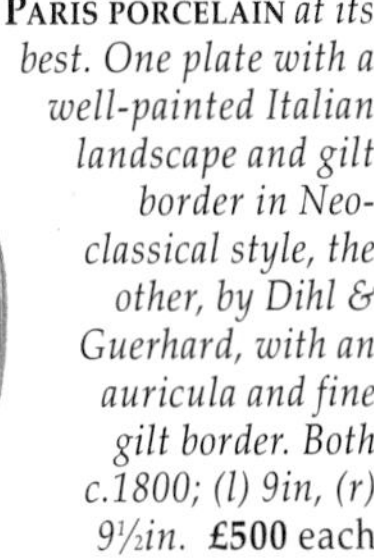

▷ **SPODE PORCELAIN DISH** *which was originally part of a large service. Typically for the time, it has a gilt border and is painted with a limodorum, which would have been copied from a botanical book or periodical. 1815; 12in long.* **£600**

▽ **PARIS PORCELAIN** *at its best. One plate with a well-painted Italian landscape and gilt border in Neo-classical style, the other, by Dihl & Guerhard, with an auricula and fine gilt border. Both c.1800; (l) 9in, (r) 9½in.* **£500** each

IRONSTONE SERVICE

In 1813, Charles James Mason patented ironstone, a hard white earthenware, and all pieces bear the name (*below right*). This dessert service, which would have contained more than 30 pieces, dates from the early years and is typical of the wares from Mason's factory. The forms, derived from silver designs, have been exaggerated: the wave to the rim of the fruit stand and the scallops on the dish are much bolder than any other maker produced, and the Chinese-style floral decoration is flamboyant (*see detail*). *c.*1820; Fruit stand **£400–£600**/Dish **£300**

Other Domestic Wares

Apart from the usual dinner wares, the 18th century saw the introduction of a wide range of additional more or less functional pieces. Many of these are no longer in use and have now made their way into the collector's cabinet. The Victorians continued the lack of squeamishness their forefathers displayed and had no qualms about making a game pie dish draped with dead rabbits and pheasants or a fish dish with highly naturalistic mackerel forming the handle. Less disturbingly, they revelled in objects that suggested their function: a honey pot in the form of a skep, a jam pot like a loaf of bread and a cow's head cheese dish. In the field of domestic wares, the tyro collector can put together a large and varied selection without overstretching himself – the field is vast and there is a range of prices from a few pounds to several thousands.

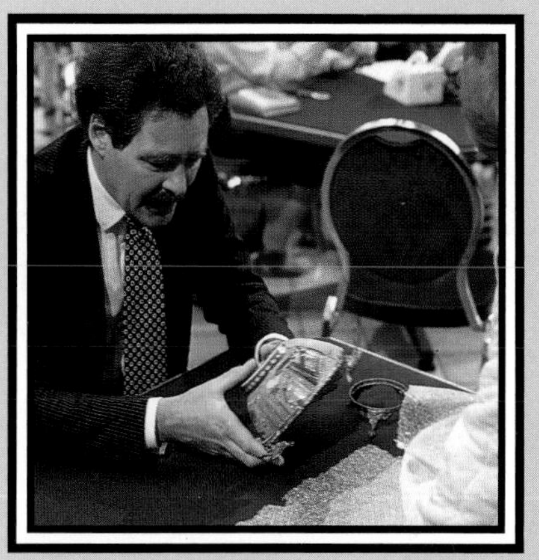

Baskets & Sweetmeat Dishes

Apart from dinner wares, many manufacturers made specialist pieces for the table. One such item was the ceramic basket, sometimes with a single overarching handle, that was intended to hold fruit, nuts or sweetmeats.

A typical example was the chestnut basket, made in the 18th century when roasted chestnuts were often served after a meal. Creamware pieces, made by Wedgwood and at Leeds, were moulded and then pierced, their fragile structure making them exceedingly prone to damage.

Ornate Rococo shells or leaves were popular shapes for sweetmeat dishes, which were usually smaller than baskets.

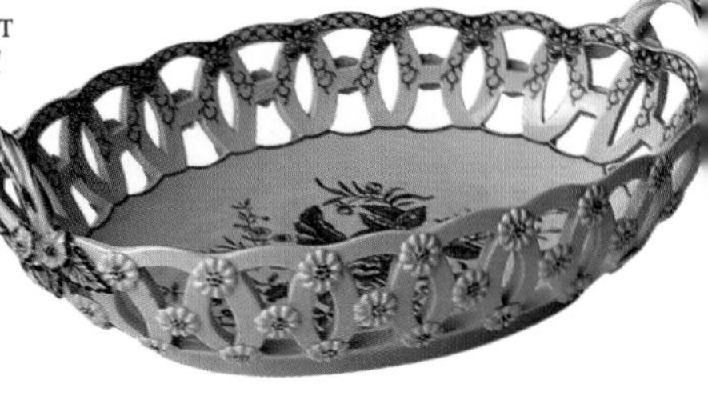

▷ **Worcester chestnut basket,** *transfer printed as were most such baskets. They have survived in fair numbers but are often damaged, in which event they sell for £100 or less. 1770; 9½in wide.* **£450**

◁ **Regency Worcester basket** *with overlapping moulded gilt leaves, a popular motif also used on Rockingham porcelain. The central scene shows a peasant family in front of a Malvern landscape (as titled on the reverse). The handle has been restored, greatly reducing the value. 1815; 10in wide.* **£800**

▷ **Sweetmeat dish** *(one of a pair) in the form of a child playing cymbals beside a shell. The black and gilt base with a "key" pattern is an unusual feature. It was made by Moore Bros., whose designs were closely modelled on those of Minton. 1880; 6in high.* **£150**

△ **Belleek basket** *The piece has been straw moulded to give a wicker effect, and is decorated with applied flowers and leaves. It would have been impractical in use and so would have been a poor seller, hence its rarity. 1900; 6in wide.* **£300**

▷ **"Rathmore" pattern basket** *This Belleek design was first made in 1904, and has been in production ever since. The fine "net" effect, typical of the factory, is effected only with great skill. The handles and feet imitate coral. 1990; 11in wide.* **£2,300**

◁ **Wemyss egg basket** *made for Thomas Goode and Sons, the main dealers in Wemyss ware. The pottery was popular with the gentry in the early 20th century. Its soft, absorbent body was easily damaged and stained and good examples are at a premium. 1900; 7in high* **£1,500**

HOUSEHOLD ITEMS

Ceramics, being generally inexpensive, durable and easily washed, are ideal for utilitarian wares. The original buyer could have pieces that were decorative as well as functional; now, divorced from use, they have become collector's items.

The antiques market is not static and there are sudden bursts of enthusiasm for a newly recognized field: cheese dishes and biscuit barrels are newcomers to the collecting world. Among the best of these uncharted buys are the millions of Chinese blue and white export plates of the second half of the 18th century, which are still relatively inexpensive.

◁ **BUTTER DISH** *One of a pair, this underglaze blue and white butter dish was made in China and exported to the West. The shell shape came from contemporary silver designs. c.1750; 5in wide.* The pair **£600–£800**

▷ **DERBY BUTTER TUB** *The enamel painting on this Derby piece is of good quality. The fine decoration, unusual shape and excellent condition all increase the value. c.1760; 5in wide.* **£1,500–£2,000**

◁ **NOVELTY JAM POT** *The cottage-loaf shape of this Royal Worcester jam pot reflects the Victorian taste for novelty food ceramics which had a visual link with the food they contained. 1900; 6in high.* **£150–£200**

△ **TWO SALTS** *The Chinese export salt (left), dating from the 1740s, was painted in the* famille-rose *palette. That on the right, made in Hungary in the 1890s, replicates armorial pieces of the 1740s. It was fired upside down leaving the top rim unglazed, a flaw disguised by the gilt border.* Both *3in wide.* Left **£100–£120**; right **£60–£80**

◁ **NOVELTY CHEESE DISH** *Made in the shape of a cow's head, this English earthenware cheese dish dates from the late Victorian period. c.1895; 7in high.* **£300**

COLLECTION OF JAPANESE JARS

These three amusing jars and covers were made in Japan during the 1920s and '30s. They are the work of two companies, the Maritomo Toki Company of Seto City and the Kahuhon Toki Company of Yokkaichi City. 2in–4in high. The group **£60–£90**

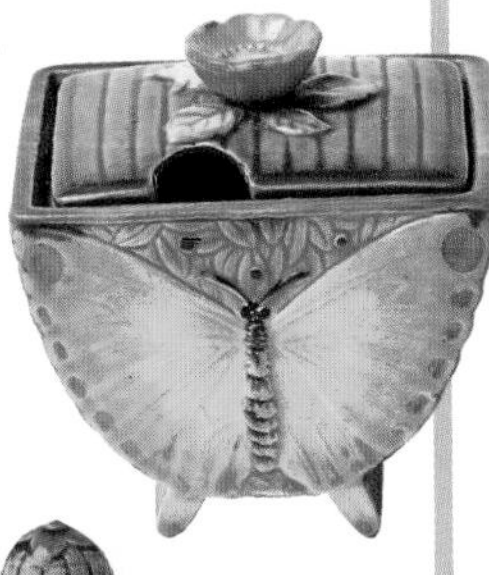

POT-POURRI DISHES

Containers made for pot-pourri, a fragrant mixture of spices and petals used to scent the air, were popular from the mid-18th century. The delftware bowl (*top*), made in the 1750s, is 8 inches wide. The slight damage barely affects its value of £1,000–£1,200. The shape of the lower dish, made at Wedgwood *c.*1815 using the famous *rosso antico* (red stoneware) body, was taken from a Greek *krater*, or bowl for mixing wine and water. It is 13½ inches wide and would fetch £300–£500 at auction.

▷ **JASPER DIP CANDLESTICKS**
One of Wedgwood's most popular innovations, jasperware is a hard, smooth, unglazed stoneware stained with metallic oxides. Originally, the clay itself was stained, but to cut costs, from 1777 the wares were given just an outer coat of colour by dipping them. In 1854, "solid" jasper was reintroduced. These attractively simple candlesticks are less popular than those that are more elaborately decorated. 1840; 9in high. **£200–£300**

◁ **SLIPWARE KNIFEBOX**
A light-coloured slip, or liquid clay, was used to contrast with the dark glaze on this knifebox. It was made around the Halifax area in the Yorkshire potteries in the mid-19th century. 11in long. **£150–£200**

▷ **MEISSEN-STYLE TEA CANISTER** *Workers from the factory took the Meissen style of decoration and the formula for hard-paste porcelain to factories in Vienna, Italy and elsewhere in Germany. One of these, Höchst, made this fine canister. Its value would be double if it had its lid. 1770s; 3½in high.* **£1,000**

◁ **STAFFORDSHIRE TEA JAR** *Made of creamware in the late 18th century, this small jar is marked "Bohea", which is black tea of rather low quality since it was the last crop of the season. The fact that the jar has sustained some damage is reflected in its value. c.1780; 4in high.* **£120–£150**

PRATTWARE SNUFFBOX

Named after a prominent Staffordshire potting family, prattware is a creamware body typically decorated in underglaze green, ochre and brown. This unusual snuffbox, made in Yorkshire, is based on the enamelled pieces made at Bilston, Staffordshire. Pictured on one end is a dog on a cushion; on the other, which unscrews to take the snuff, is the inscription " E.O. 1795". 2in high. **£1,000**

Vessels for storing and serving alcohol have existed for thousands of years; the earliest, such as ancient Greek wine jars, are now museum pieces. Highly prized, however, are German stoneware tankards and jugs, made since the Middle Ages, and English delftware wine bottles from the 17th century; later copies are plentiful but less valuable.

In about 1700, the vogue for drinking punch – a mixture of alcohol and spices – led to specialist punch bowls. The drink was mixed in these vessels and served using a ladle. Both delftware and Chinese examples are sought after and the best can make thousands of pounds at auction.

Also of interest to collectors are the decorative barrels used in Victorian public houses or bars for storing spirits or beer.

BARRELS FOR SPIRITS

SALT-GLAZED STONEWARE BRANDY BARREL *The decoration takes the form of a knight on horseback and a lion* couchant. *Although many barrels survive, rarely is one found in such good condition. c.1830; 10½in.* **£600**

◁ **FAMILLE-ROSE PUNCH BOWL** *in the palette known as Mandarin, which included a purple-pink. Pieces decorated with European subjects, such as this hunting scene, are usually more expensive than those with Chinese designs. c.1760; 11in wide.* **£1,800–£2,000**

▷ **PEARLWARE PUNCH BOWL** *transfer printed with Romantic rustic scenes of medieval castles, ruins and cottages. This piece was made by one of the Staffordshire factories. c.1820; 11in wide.* **£120–£150**

EARTHENWARE GIN BARREL *Although these wares were generally unmarked, this well-decorated example bears the Belleek factory mark and date, which make it more desirable. 1877; 11in high.* **£500–£700**

△ **GERMAN STEIN, OR TANKARD,** *made of porcelain and decorated with a landscape reminiscent of Dutch Delft. The base bears a lithophane – a low relief which produces a tonal picture when it is held to the light. 1890–1910; 8in high.* **£100**

▷ **"REMBRANDTWARE" JUG** *made at Doulton by the studio head, Charles Noke, who was noted for his use of experimental glazes on useful and domestic wares. It advertises Dewar's whisky. Pieces such as this are becoming increasingly collectable. 1910–20; 7in high.* **£150**

Bedroom & Toilet Wares

It was not until after World War II that the majority of houses in Britain had indoor bathrooms. Before that time, most people's morning wash entailed using a basin of water poured from a ewer.

The simplest bedroom sets included a matching ewer, basin and soap dish, although more elaborate sets also had a sponge bowl, toothbrush holder and two chamber pots, which were kept in a bedside cupboard, known as a commode.

Since these sets are now redundant, they are often split up. In America, it is rumoured that the chamber pots are sometimes used as punch bowls.

△ **Sunderland basin and ewer** *The pink lustre borders on these pieces are typical of Sunderland wares. They have been in production on and off since the early 19th century. The quality of the potting, the prints and the pink lustre varies according to the date at which they were made. Reproductions made in the 1920s are the most deceptive.*

This set is decorated with transfer prints of the bridge over the River Wear on the outside of the basin and poems on a watery theme inside the basin and on the jug. c.1840; Basin *12in wide*/Jug *9in high.* **£300**

△ **Belleek bedroom set** *Although Belleek wares are popular, plain pieces are less sought after. If these were decorated, the value would be double, but without the factory mark their value would be under £40. c.1870;* Jug *9in high.* **£150**

▷ **EWER AND BASIN** *Made in Staffordshire in the late 19th century, this ewer and matching basin were transfer printed. The transfer-printed design was hand coloured, often by children, and was far cheaper than hand painting. c.1890;* Jug *15in high.* **£150–£200**

◁ **EWER AND BASIN** *transfer printed with flowers in underglaze blue. The Gater, Hall & Co. factory where it was made changed hands – and thus marks – several times, and dating can, therefore, be precise.* 1914; Jug *14in high.* **£50**

▷ **EARTHENWARE BEDROOM SET** *This set, by Thomas Lawrence of Longton, a small factory at Stoke-on-Trent, was decorated using both hand painting and spraying. The jars and chamber pot (not shown) enhance the value of the set. c.1925;* Jug *15in high.* **£100**

CHAMBER POT

Hand painted with orange and yellow daffodils over a transfer, this Doulton chamber pot has the registration number 258549 and is marked England. A matching ewer and basin would fetch £150–£250. *c.*1895; 14in across. **£25–£30**

Bedroom and toilet ceramics are not limited to chamber pots and ewer and basin sets. The lady of the house would need her dressing table equipment and, before the advent of electric light, candlesticks and tapersticks were essential. Inevitably, objects in daily use were most likely to be damaged and, like the barbers' bowls, may now fetch considerable sums if perfect. Today few of these items would be used, they are for decoration only.

△ **DERBY TAPERSTICK** *This piece is decorated in one of the Derby factory's popular Imari-inspired patterns. In perfect condition and complete with the candle snuffer, its value would be greater. 1810; 3in high.* **£150–£200**

◁ **TAPERSTICK** *Fine and rare taperstick with some damage. It is, however, still interesting to collectors since it has the Worcester mark and is decorated with the attractive Japanese-type pattern known as "Finger and Thumb". c.1800; 2in high.* **£200–£250;** In perfect condition **£800**

△ **BARBERS' BOWLS,** *identified by the moon-shaped gap that fitted the neck of the man being shaved, were imported from the Far East in quantity. The bowl on the right was made c.1710 at Arita in Japan and decorated in underglaze blue, iron-red, green enamel and gilding. The other bowl was made in China about 30 years later and decorated in the Japanese Imari palette, which was highly fashionable at the time.* Both bowls *12in.* Each **£700–£1,000**.

△ **GERMAN DRESSING TABLE SET** *This rather poor-quality porcelain set was made toward the end of the 19th century. The Neo-classical scenes have been transfer printed, as has the gilding. Almost identical pieces are still being made, a fact which is reflected in the low price. 1890s;* Tray *12in long.* **£200–£300**

◁△ **DRESSING TABLE SET** *Twenty years after the Derby factory was established c.1750, it began to decorate its porcelain in Japanese Imari style. More than 100 years later, this dressing table set was hand painted with similar designs. By that time, the factory had been renamed Royal Crown Derby, after Queen Victoria's visit in 1890. This set includes assorted pots and jars, a tray, candlesticks and a ringstand (left). 1890;* Tray *9in long.* **£1,000**

Caring for your Valuables

Antiques may be bought for their beauty, craftsmanship, history, rarity, or even for their curiosity value. It does not matter whether you are buying an item because it gives you pleasure, or because you consider it to be a serious investment. It is important to see that it is well looked after and properly insured. That way, it can be enjoyed today and handed down from generation to generation.

One of the chief joys of collecting antique ceramics must be that most wares were made for a practical purpose, and there is no reason why a careful owner should not continue to use them in the same way. How much more memorable to serve tea from an antique tea set or to hold a dinner party at which your guests dine from century-old plates.

Similarly, it is perfectly acceptable to display cut flowers in an antique vase, provided the water is held in a separate container to prevent staining. Earthenware and ceramics with a crazed glaze, such as bone china and some soft-paste porcelain, are water permeable, while hard-paste porcelain and stoneware are not.

More delicate pieces should be kept only for display on secure shelves or in cabinets, preferably locked. Take particular care with lids and areas which have been restored or are cracked.

Caring for ceramics

1 All antique ceramics should be washed by hand – never put them in a dishwasher.
2 When a plate or dish has been used for cheese or any other fatty food, wash it immediately. Oily substances are difficult, if not impossible, to remove once they have penetrated the body.
3 Do not immerse any earthenware with an unglazed foot rim or cracks, since moisture will be absorbed and the piece may become discoloured. It is safer to wipe it with a cloth or cottonwool dipped in warm water containing a little mild detergent.
4 Use a shower attachment when washing flower-encrusted and other delicate items, then leave them to dry. If you dry such pieces with a tea towel, you run the risk of its snagging and breaking off pieces of the porcelain.
5 Do not handle unglazed pottery with unclean hands, since greasy fingerprints may mark the piece permanently.

6 Household bleach or cleaner containing chlorine should not be used on ceramics. If hard- or soft-paste porcelain is discoloured, the staining can sometimes be removed by using a 20 percent solution of hydrogen peroxide, which is available from chemists, with a few drops of ammonia added. Wearing rubber gloves, dip strips of cottonwool in the solution and lay them on the stain for about an hour, but do not let them dry on the surface. Repeat if the stain has not disappeared. This treatment is not suitable for pieces with any gilding or lustre decoration or with pale blue or greenish 19th-century enamelling.
7 Do not warm porcelain plates and tureens in the oven, even at the coolest setting, since the glaze may craze. Heat them by placing them in hot water for a minute or two, then dry carefully.
8 Cups, mugs, jugs and teapots should be held by the body, with the base supported, never by the handle alone.

9 When hanging plates on the wall, always use the plastic-coated plate hangers that can be adjusted to fit individual plates; they are available from all good china shops. Stick-on plate hangers may remove the glaze from delft and majolica. Never hang cracked plates on the wall.

10 Good pieces of pottery or porcelain should be repaired or restored only by professionals. If an item is broken, collect all the pieces, even the tiniest, wrap them in paper and take them to a professional restorer.
11 Unless you want to sell a piece, do not have it restored or any damage repaired, provided it does not offend you.
12 When moving ceramics, never pack them in tea towels or fabric of any kind in case the material snags and damages the pieces; use bubblewrap or even newspaper. Pack plates vertically, do not stack them one on top of the other.

INSURANCE

The question of insurance is a matter of personal choice, and insurance companies vary greatly in the types of cover they provide, and in the cost of the premiums. Cover for very valuable antiques can be expensive, but trying to find the lowest quotation is not necessarily the wisest course. Specialist brokers, as well as building society insurance services, understand the needs of collectors.

The first thing to do is to decide on the nature of the cover you require: the kind of "risks". Comprehensive and All In policies cover only certain specified perils, such as theft, fire, explosion, water damage or storm damage. In the event of theft, evidence will be required before a claim is met, and insurance companies will ask if the police have been notified.

Another type of cover is All Risks, which represents the maximum cover you are likely to obtain. It will also cover you against accidental breakage and disappearance, but not "inherent vice", such as the progressive deterioration of glazes on some earthenware items as a result of atmospheric conditions.

Decide exactly what you want to insure and list the items with as much detail as possible. If your collection consists of a number of small items, such as snuffboxes, jugs or cups and saucers, you may need to list them all. It is advisable to keep receipts as back-up evidence if you have to make a claim. Sometimes insurance companies ask to see photographs, credit card vouchers or notes of any distinguishing marks as well.

You may even need to consider a policy that covers your possessions away from home, as when they are sent to a restorer or if you take them to an antiques fair for the purpose of selling them.

VALUING YOUR POSSESSIONS

If you want to get a valuation of items you have inherited or had for some time, it is usually a good idea to obtain two quotes: from either reputable dealers or auction houses. (You may have to pay them a small percentage of the value.)

Most insurance valuations are based on the full market price, or replacement cost, of an item. That is why it is important to give your insurers as much detail as possible. For example, where plates, mugs or tea sets are kept and how they are protected. If you under-insure, insurance companies are likely to scale down their pay-outs – or may even refuse to pay out at all.

It is now fairly standard practice for an insurer not to pay a claim in cash, but to settle the claim once you have bought a replacement. Frequently you are expected to pay an "excess", which can be, for example, the first £25 of the cost of each claim.

Index-linked policies automatically adjust the amount of insurance cover, and your premiums, annually. But it is still worth checking the figures from time to time. It is a good idea to have valuations updated every few years because fantastic appreciation often occurs with certain periods or pieces.

LOOKING AFTER YOUR ANTIQUES

Insurers are very keen that you take "reasonable" care of valuable items. Store ceramics at an even

temperature in a dry place. Make certain that shelves are strong enough to support the weight of the items you place on them. For instance, don't keep a precious china object on a narrow, flimsy shelf in a hallway where people may knock it as they put their coats on.

It also makes sense to install smoke detectors, particularly in living areas, and to have fire extinguishers easily to hand.

If something does get broken or damaged, get the written approval of your insurance company before having it restored.

Security

According to research, 1 in 12 households is burgled each year. By joining a Neighbourhood Watch scheme, not only can the risk be reduced to 1 in 75, but you could also lower the cost of your home contents premium. The local Crime Prevention Officer will be happy to help you set up a scheme if none exists. Usually you need half the people in your area – whether it is a street or block of flats – to agree to join.

Normally your Crime Prevention Officer will also be happy to advise you if the locks and bolts on your house are adequate. Security devices such as five-lever mortise locks on doors and key-operated window locks are fairly inexpensive to fit and highly effective; they may even help to reduce the cost of your premiums.

As a rule, two mortise deadlocks should be fitted to each external door, and window locks to all ground-floor and first-floor windows. Vulnerable windows, such as those in a basement or one that can be easily reached from a flat roof or drain pipe, should be fitted with iron bars. Additional precautions, such as security bolts on doors, are worth considering, especially where a door is not made of solid timber or is less than 1¾ inches thick.

Another way to deter burglars is to fit an alarm. This can also reduce your premiums, but don't go for the cheapest quote just to save a few pounds. You should choose a recognized organization that offers local maintenance facilities and a full guarantee. The local police or your insurers will probably be able to recommend appropriate companies to you.

If your home does get burgled, you should report the matter at the police station and to your insurers without delay.

National & Provincial Building Society, whose support helped to make this book possible, offers the insurance services the collector requires. Advice is available from its branches, or call the advice line on Freefone 0800 80 80 80.

Collector's Checklist

Ceramics probably have a wider appeal than any other works of art, and most households possess at least one or two interesting items. Many delightful pieces can be bought very cheaply indeed: for instance, you can pick up a 200-year-old plate for less than a pound if you do not mind a hairline crack. At the other extreme are incredibly expensive items, such as a Chinese pottery horse made during the Tang Dynasty (618–907) which sold recently for more than £3,000,000.

The relatively small size of pottery and porcelain objects is an additional reason for their popularity: you can keep adding to your collection without too much risk of running out of space. The broad range of materials, styles, factories – and even decorators – involved gives the collector a wide choice of fields in which to specialize.

Ceramics are often colourful, dramatic and of practical use, factors that have attracted interior decorators as well as more traditional collectors. If you find that objects in your chosen field have become "fashionable" and prices have consequently skyrocketed, remember that many categories overlap and it may be possible to increase your collection with pieces from a related field which are more competitively priced. For instance, while large decorative plates and chargers find a ready market, bowls, since they are less easy to display, may be freely available.

There are probably more fakes, forgeries and reproductions of ceramics than of any other type of antique. A fake is a genuine piece that has been altered, a forgery is an attempt to deceive, while a reproduction is an honest re-creation of an earlier object.

Many early deceptions – such as Worcester and Derby pieces with fake Meissen marks – are now accepted and even sought after by collectors.

Problems tend to arise when reproductions are sold as the genuine article, making them forgeries. A prime example of this is the number of Korean copies of Chinese *famille-rose* and Canton porcelain that were imported merely as decorative items but are now appearing at some small auctions and in some antiques shops in the guise of original pieces.

Every so often a particularly clever deception fools the antiques market. The best measure a collector can take when buying a piece is to question the seller closely; thoroughly examine the item; and remember that fakes are most likely to be produced when the value of originals is extremely high.

Restoration of a piece often reduces its value because it creates doubt as to the degree of damage the restoration may hide.

There can be no substitute for experience and for knowing your field when purchasing old ceramics. It is difficult, for instance, for a beginner to tell some pottery from porcelain, but after examining a variety of pieces this becomes easier. So make a point of inspecting and handling as many pieces as possible, and bear in mind the following points.

Tips for buyers

1 Before even thinking about buying ceramics there are three essential things to learn: the difference between pottery and porcelain; the difference between hard- and soft-paste porcelain; and the difference between hand-painted and printed wares.

2 When buying a piece of pottery or porcelain, always assume that there is something wrong with it and that the person selling it knows but is not telling.

3 If a small amount of damage is pointed out to you, check the item carefully for further damage.

4 Does the seller answer your questions openly, or is there a hint of evasion? If so, be wary about buying from that source. If an item seems exceptionally cheap, ask yourself whether you have really found a bargain or whether you are being conned.

5 Check that the material, style, coloration, painting, modelling and gilding are all consistent with the period in which the item was supposed to have been made. Satisfy yourself that the piece is up to the aesthetic standard usual for the factory in question. Poor painting and the use of the wrong colours are often signs of a fake.

6 If the item you wish to buy has a mark, is it the one you would expect to find on a piece of this date and is it the correct size and in the right position? Fakes of the Chelsea red anchor mark, for example, are often too big.

7 Always ask whether a piece has been restored. If the answer is yes, ask the dealer to what extent; if the answer is no or don't know, ask whether you can test it with a pin (which will glide over original glaze and catch on softer restoration work). If the dealer refuses to allow you to do this, take your custom elsewhere.

8 Prices on tickets are often open to negotiation. Do not be afraid to offer a lower amount.

9 Make sure that the seller gives you a full receipt, including date, attribution and condition report.

Collections of interest

British Museum
Museum Street
London WC1B 3DG
Telephone: 0171 636 1555
Burrell Collection
Pollock Country Park
Glasgow G43 1AT
Telephone: 0141 649 7151
Glaisher Collection
Fitzwilliam Museum
Cambridge CB2 1RB
Telephone: 01223 332 900
Victoria & Albert Museum
Cromwell Road, London SW7 2RL
Telephone: 0171 938 8500
Wallace Collection
Manchester Square
London W1M 6BN
Telephone: 0171 935 0687

In addition, many provincial museums have collections of locally made ceramics, and most of the major manufacturers have their own museums and offer tours around their factories.

Glossary

Note: SMALL CAPITALS within an entry refer to another entry.

A

Aesthetic Movement Decorative arts movement, much influenced by Oriental styles, which flourished in Britain and America *c.*1870–80.
Agate ware Staffordshire pottery made to resemble the colour and marbling of natural agate. It was popular in the 18th C.
Applied decoration An ornamental finish prepared in advance and applied to an object in a completed state, as with the motifs on WEDGWOOD'S jasperware.
Art Deco A style of art and decoration, reflecting the modern aesthetic of the machine age, which developed in the 20th C between the two world wars. This style was first popularized at the 1925 *Exposition des Arts Décoratifs* in Paris, from which the term Art Deco is derived.

B

Basalt Black, fine-grained stoneware developed by several Staffordshire potters and improved by Josiah WEDGWOOD in the mid-1760s. This relatively cheap material was used to manufacture vases, copies of Classical bronzes and cameos.
Belleek Factory in County Fermanagh, Northern Ireland, established in 1857 and specializing in woven parian PORCELAIN with motifs drawn from local flora and fauna. It also produced delicate, pearlized tableware.
Biscuit pottery Term describing all ceramics that have been fired once but not glazed.
Blanc-de-Chine French term for unpainted, highly translucent PORCELAIN made in Fujian Province, China, which is characterized by a thick glaze. It was much copied by European factories in the 18th C.
Blue and white Decorative colour scheme for pottery and PORCELAIN using COBALT BLUE as an underglaze pigment.
Body The mixture of raw materials from which pottery or PORCELAIN is made. Often called "paste" when referring to porcelain.
Bone china A mixture of bone ash and kaolin which makes a hard, stable PORCELAIN. Introduced by SPODE in 1794.
Bow The largest 18th-C PORCELAIN factory in Britain, also known as New Canton. Founded in 1744 by Thomas Frye, it took advantage of the new soft-paste porcelain, invented in 1748, to produce imitation Oriental porcelain and BLUE AND WHITE wares. Both figures and tablewares were made.

C

Chelsea One of the earliest PORCELAIN factories in Britain. It was founded in 1745 and flourished until 1769 when it was sold to DERBY. Its output was devoted to tablewares, tea sets and vases for the luxury market.
Chinoiserie European imitations of Chinese decoration and design – in particular, fretwork, Oriental motifs and carving. Not to be confused with Chinese articles exported to Europe.
Clobbering Overpainting an existing design on ceramics with coloured ENAMELS or gilding. Chinese BLUE AND WHITE was often treated in this way, particularly by the Dutch.
Coalport Shropshire-based PORCELAIN factory established in 1795; famous for its smooth, translucent BONE CHINA developed after 1810. In 1821 a maroon ground was introduced which became a Coalport characteristic. During the 1830s the factory produced popular flower-encrusted Rococo vases and other pieces. The factory was acquired by the WEDGWOOD group and ceased production in 1926.
Cobalt blue Pigment derived from cobalt oxide which could be fired at high temperature without changing colour; much used on early ceramics. *Cf.* BLUE AND WHITE
Creamware Cheap, cream-coloured

EARTHENWARE, made from Devon clay and ground burnt flints, with a transparent glaze. It was refined in the 1760s by Josiah WEDGWOOD, when it was known as "Queen's Ware", and soon became the standard domestic pottery used in Britain.

D

DELFT Centre in Holland for tin-glazed EARTHENWARE where Dutch potters adapted the designs on Chinese BLUE AND WHITE PORCELAIN from the mid-16th C to the mid-18th C. This largely domestic pottery was very successful until the emergence of CREAMWARE and porcelain, which became freely available at the end of the 18th C.

DELFTWARE Tin-glazed pottery, inspired by Dutch wares, made in England during the 17th C and 18th C.

DERBY The first factory began producing Meissen imitations in soft-paste PORCELAIN in 1750. In the 1770s, the Japanese IMARI style became strongly identified with Derby. In the early 19th C, BONE CHINA replaced soft-paste porcelain and the company produced less expensive products until 1848, when it closed. The Crown Derby Porcelain Company was set up in 1876 to produce decorated and gilded bone china once again.

DOULTON Factory in Lambeth, London, founded by John Doulton (1793–1873). Initially, it produced household stoneware, but later involvement with the Lambeth School of Art led to the development of the Doulton Studio art pottery in the 1860s. The factory also created Lambeth FAIENCE and silicon and marquetry wares; in 1882, it launched high-quality figures and tile panels in PORCELAIN.

E

EARTHENWARE Porous pottery, fired at *c.*900–1,500°F, which is waterproof only when glazed. The colour of the clays used and the metal oxide content produce a varied range of colours.

ENAMEL Form of decoration that can be fused to metal, glass or ceramics. It is made from a mixture of powdered glass and pigmented metallic oxides, suspended in an oily medium. During firing, the oily medium burns off and the other constituents fuse.

F

FAIENCE French term for tin-glazed EARTHENWARE. *See also* DELFTWARE

FAMILLE ROSE "Pink family"; opaque ENAMELS used on Chinese PORCELAIN in 1723–35, the most conspicuous colour being rose-pink (derived from gold).

FAMILLE VERTE "Green family"; transparent ENAMELS, especially brilliant green, used to decorate Chinese Kangxi-period (1661–1722) PORCELAIN.

FELDSPAR PORCELAIN BONE CHINA which contains pure feldspar rather than china stone and so is much tougher. First produced by COALPORT, but soon taken up by SPODE.

I

IMARI WARE Japanese porcelain, made at Arita from the 17th C onward, with panelled decoration drawn from local textile designs in underglaze blue, iron-red ENAMEL and gilding, with some use of black, green and yellow enamels. Imari patterns inspired many European manufacturers in the 18th C and 19th C, among them DERBY and SPODE.

IMPRESSED MARK Pottery mark, where a row of letters or marks is stamped into the soft, unfired clay. Used on early pieces from BOW.

INCISED MARK The earliest method of marking pottery in which the mark is scratched into the soft clay before firing; the edges often feel rough.

J

JAPANNING Technique originating in the early 18th C whereby European craftsmen imitated Oriental lacquerwork with paint and varnish.

JAPONAISERIE European designs and forms influenced by Japanese style.

K

KAKIEMON WARE 17th-C Japanese porcelain vividly coloured in turquoise, dark blue, red and black and decorated with plants and birds. Widely imitated in European porcelain in the 18th C.

KRAAK Chinese porcelain, decorated in underglaze blue, exported to Holland in the late 16th C and early 17th C. The name is a corruption of "carrack", the ship used to transport it.

L

LUSTREWARE Pottery or PORCELAIN to which a metallic glaze containing silver, copper, gold or platinum is applied to produce a sheen.

M

MAJOLICA Vividly decorated EARTHENWARE, moulded or pressed to produce a sharp relief. It was developed by Herbert Minton in 1851.
MINTON Factory established in 1793 by Thomas Minton, well known during the 19th C for MAJOLICA, parian and *cloisonné* work. Minton has continued to produce high-quality PORCELAIN in the 20th C.

P

PORCELAIN Hard translucent white substance made from china clay and china stone. Hard-paste porcelain is fired at a higher temperature than soft paste and is cold to the touch. Soft paste is warmer and has a softer glaze.
POTTERY Term used for a wide variety of materials, including EARTHENWARE and stoneware, made from baked clay.

S

SLIP Potter's clay reduced to a creamy consistency, used to coat pottery or as an adhesive for external decoration. It is also used to cast hollow figures.
SLIPWARE Any pottery decorated with SLIP; this can take the form of dipping the article in slip or trailing thickened slip across the surface of a body.
SPODE Factory founded by Josiah Spode in 1770, initially producing domestic EARTHENWARE, including CREAMWARE and TRANSFER-PRINTED Staffordshire blue, which Spode pioneered. After 1797 Spode produced BONE CHINA tableware and, from 1800, translucent FELDSPAR PORCELAIN and worked with ENAMEL decoration in the Regency style. In 1846 the Spode factory, known as Copeland since 1833, perfected parian ware. Copeland, using the Spode trademark, continues to produce high-quality tablewares to this day.
SPRIGGING Ceramic decoration, shaped separately, then attached or "sprigged" to the main body with SLIP.
STAFFORDSHIRE POTTERIES British ceramics factories concentrated around the towns of Stoke-on-Trent, Burslem, Hanley, Tunstall, Longton and Fenton, which exploited the local clays and the abundant supplies of coal. Most of the innovative techniques in British ceramics have come from the Staffordshire potteries.

T

TRANSFER PRINTING Method of applying decoration to mass-produced ceramics. Paper, printed with a design in metallic oxides, is wrapped around the porcelain and burnt away during firing, leaving the pattern in the glaze. It was invented in Britain in the mid-18th C and is still the most common method of decorating ceramics throughout Europe and America.

W

WEDGWOOD British pottery founded by Josiah Wedgwood (1730–95) in 1759 at Burslem, Staffordshire. Its reputation stems from its many innovations in ceramics, designed to rival imported Chinese PORCELAIN, which included BASALT, CREAMWARE, pearlware and the blue jasperware synonymous with its name.
WORCESTER British factory founded in 1751 and still active. Early output concentrated on soft-paste PORCELAIN decorated in underglaze blue and modelled on silverware shapes. After 1763 there was a move toward the luxury market with imitations of Meissen, Sèvres and Japanese designs. BONE CHINA was introduced in 1800 and decorated by a neighbouring factory, Chamberlains; the two companies merged in 1840. During the 19th C, Worcester produced richly gilded and enamelled tablewares, figures, parian ware and Renaissance-style vases.

Index

This index should be used in conjunction with the glossary.

M000049945

POSITIVE NUTRITION

STRATEGIC EATING TO UPGRADE YOUR HEALTH AND ENERGY

KATE COOK

Good Health!
Vitality 2019
Go well
[illegible] & all at BM.

Published by
LID Publishing Limited
The Record Hall, Studio 204,
16-16a Baldwins Gardens,
London EC1N 7RJ, UK

524 Broadway, 11th Floor, Suite 08-120,
New York, NY 10012, US

info@lidpublishing.com
www.lidpublishing.com

A member of:

www.businesspublishersroundtable.com

Printed in the Czech Republic by Finidr

ISBN: 978-1-911498-65-0

Cover and page design: Caroline Li

POSITIVE NUTRITION

STRATEGIC EATING TO UPGRADE YOUR HEALTH AND ENERGY

KATE COOK

LONDON NEW YORK BOGOTA
MADRID BARCELONA BUENOS AIRES
MEXICO CITY MONTERREY SAN FRANCISCO
SHANGHAI

CONTENTS

To Mike Burton
(1933 - 2017)
A Life Well Lived

INTRODUCTION

"It is a truth universally acknowledged, that a single man in possession of a good fortune must be in want of a wife."

Jane Austen, *Pride and Prejudice*

I am not in the business of upstaging Jane Austen but, in the nutrition world, it is a truth universally unacknowledged that most people don't actually make the connection between what they eat and how they feel.

Knowing is one thing and *living it* is another.

Making the connection between what you eat and how you feel seems obvious, right? It is amazing that we don't really *live* that connection. We are so darned busy, food is just the fuel that gets us from one meeting to another. And we think tomorrow it will all be better, and we will make the time. Yes, sure, we all would love to grow our own mung beans on our windowsill, but we just don't have time right now! Let me just finish one last email. Hang on, that's my cunning iPhone with its annoying and repetitive jingle: Nag. Bleep. Buzz. Zip. Whirr. Bing. Bing. Bing.

This disconnect is complicated, encompassing industrialization, consumerism, modern convenience food, long working hours, and time, or lack of it.

In our modern world, all the time-saving devices that were supposed to liberate us have instead enslaved us, turning us into **machines**. Technology has drawn us in, and our very reliance on it makes it seem as though Homo Sapiens are exempt from the effects of biochemistry. I am not just blaming technology. However, this is one of the things – along with work, money and a busy lifestyle – that we rarely step away from and look at the cost to ourselves, others, the environment, and our planet.

Strategic eating means that you have a blueprint and a map of the food landscape, and you know how to navigate it with confidence.

We forget that essentially we are hairless, fat-storing apes with many of the same supressed (or not) instincts or desires as other animals. Our logic tells us that we must be above these other animals, who lack the social grace of using a napkin. We, the mighty human, have a universal pass, exempting us from how food affects us or our health. Wouldn't our fellow omnivore, the pig, get sick if we fed her sugar and party food? It must be because we wear clothes that we're excluded from this biological small print. That explains it!

We have always been a bit more complex in terms of how we form social groups. Our hunter-gatherer ancestors may owe their survival and our evolution to our basic need to communicate and work together. Yet now, we sit by ourselves in our individual work booths, surrounded by the plastic wrapper of an old sandwich, stuffing our faces while surfing the internet for the cricket scores. Alone! Crumbs down the keyboard are the least of our worries. The industrialized complex environment that we work in is a reflection of the enclosures that mass-produced farmed animals live in. Hmm. Nice.

Are we really designed for this life? If this is our reality, how can we mitigate the effects of this transition from free-living hunter-gatherer (which probably wasn't all it was cracked up to be, by the way) to a tech man? How can we actually flourish in this relatively new environment and live a life full of vibrant health and vitality? Once we have reclaimed energy and dynamism in spades, what can we do with the surplus to change the relationship with our family, our community and our world? The important thing to do is start with yourself, and claim, with both hands, a life well lived. Connected. Experiencing all of it, moment by moment.

The magic door to this life is food. We all have to eat to nourish and flourish.

Strategic eating means that you have a blueprint and a map of the food landscape, and you know how to navigate it with confidence. Eating strategically delivers dynamic energy, restful sleep, critical concentration and a responsive immune system, delivering a sense of happiness with enthusiasm to spare. Eating mindlessly, randomly grabbing stuff on the go, leaves you with the energy of a sloth, with the ultimate cost of not living in that space of connection. It's your choice.

PART 1
YOUR NUTRITIONAL BEST FOR THE PLANET

You know the old saying about there being no such thing as a free lunch? The deal is you have to give something back. You'll have energy to spare, which is great. I would encourage you to use the focussed dynamism and enthusiasm to feel amazing and have the capacity to nurture your family, your community and your planet by using your food 'dollar' wisely. It's a perception and a choice, but that choice has far-reaching effects in your local economy. And before our planet is entirely concreted over, your food decisions might just be important for not only your future, but your children's too. Of course, currently we really do not have 'food democracy' in terms of knowledge and access. But once we have nurtured ourselves, could we have space to change that, even in a small way?

HOW DID WE GET HERE?

You are obviously someone who is interested in nutrition, food and health, but have we collectively lost our confidence around food? We constantly feel we need to get the advice of the next expert or guru. Those gurus seem to have an immediate one-size-fits-all solution, usually focussing on just one area – for example, *The Gut Makeover* or *The Depression Miracle* – without looking at the whole and at us as individuals. Moreover, these gurus look beautiful, slim and perfect – leave us poor mortals alone! We feel like a failure before we even buy the book. We lose our confidence around food. An expert has to tell us what to eat. We don't feel we can make our own good decisions around food and what nurtures us as individuals.

There is a lot of debate around what is the perfect diet and how humans have managed to become the most powerful force on the planet. There are as many different eating patterns and theories as there are stars in the sky, but what seems to unite the ones that deliver good health and longevity is the notion of **real food from basic fresh ingredients** – hardly brain surgery.

Humans have a varied 'perfect diet'. From Inuit, who eat seal blubber (and only scraps of moss for veg, it seems) to the Maasai on the plains of Kenya, who seem to live perfectly well on a diet largely made up of blood and milk. The indigenous people of Australia eat witchetty grubs.

Do all these populations have a perfect diet? Probably not, but one thing they all share is that they are not made up of processed food – they are made up of fresh food found in nature. By that definition, the Western industrialized, processed diet is probably not one of these 'perfect' diets. Even those thinking they have cracked the code on good health tend to be ultra-anxious about food and obsess over which new fad will deliver the elixir of life. They stress the point by manically over-exercising (thereby creating inflammation), or eating from a very limited palette of food because they think they have found the true path to food enlightenment. Of course, there are a few 'bio-hacks' and there are a few things worth knowing in terms of nutritional science. But we should relax about food and diet and focus on some underlying principles that are worth absorbing if we want to have a life well lived.

There is a lot of debate around what is the perfect diet and how humans have managed to become the most powerful force on the planet.

+ NUTRITION INFORMATION NUB

- If you have low energy or any health issues, it's your diet (or lifestyle) that you need to address.

- If you are not eating fresh food because you haven't got the time, you may run out of time eventually (loads of time when you are dead, or worse - sick)!

- If you want to play the game of life at the top, and have loads of energy to spare for your family and community, always prioritize quality over being pinched for time. Apparently in Bali they have no concept of time. In their language, they don't have past or future tenses. Look how chilled out they seem.

- If you want to drop the term 'work-life balance' and just live by the phrase 'life', then strategic eating is for you.

- Bio-hacks are good (within reason - bio-hacks are shortcuts to upgrading your health by adding in a few chosen strategies). However, obsession is bad. Baking broccoli bread at 5am is madness (unless that really floats your boat). Learn what makes you feel good and then make it simple enough that you just get on and do it. There is no point in starting a new regime (with all good intentions), but realistically not being able to follow through on it.

- Thinking one particular diet or fad is *the only true path* is only partly true. There are plenty of paths. Look holistically. Look at yourself: are you contributing to your health issues, but expecting different results? This is the definition of insanity. Are you suboptimal because you are stressed and expect diet alone to fix it?

- Helping yourself helps everyone. Choosing your food wisely, prioritizing quality and, where possible, locally grown produce, can help start a revolution.

PART 2
YOUR BODY HEALTH. YOUR BRAIN HEALTH

Stunning news flash: your head and your body are actually attached to each other. Really.

The confusion that head and body health are separate lies in the illusion that we have one thing called 'mental health' and another called 'physical health' and that they are in completely different spheres. We think that poor mental health can be fixed through stress-reduction and blame mental health issues on past experience and trauma. Certainly that can be a huge factor, and I am absolutely not dismissing the importance of examining those aspects, but we must learn to look holistically as well. We must view ourselves as complex animals, with many intertwining factors and systems that make up who we are. Even the word *human* implies that we are not attached to the animal kingdom (we have named ourselves, after all).

Biochemistry can lead us to behave in certain ways a good portion of the time, if not all the time. For example, some people cannot process (metabolize) food and nutrients, or stress, or the effects of their environment like others can. There is a complex and delicate balance and interrelationship between different neurochemicals. For instance, serotonin (the so-called happy hormone) and dopamine (the reward hormone) have a complex interplay between them. Then there are the brain chemicals that have an intricate feed-back mechanism like other systems in the body – when one element gets too high, a feedback loop switches signals off. These hormones work on co-factors (other ingredients), which make them work properly (or not). They can either make you content (serotonin) or addicted (dopamine).

Your biochemistry needs many different nutrient co-factors, including zinc, B6 and magnesium, to convert the raw material, the amino acid L-tryptophan (which you get through your food), to mood-boosting serotonin. No amount of talking therapy is going to change how a poor diet and lifestyle will contribute to that poor conversion. You can chat about it all you want, but eating 'twaddle food' will not boost your serotonin. Twaddle food, which I am afraid is one of my own terms, is any industrialized packaged food, devoid of nutrients; 'food-like' substances, including empty white carbohydrates. They give you nothing in return. A really lengthy expiration date is another clue. If you had a pet pig that you loved and cherished, would you feed her those substances? If the answer is no – it's twaddle food, and you should avoid it.

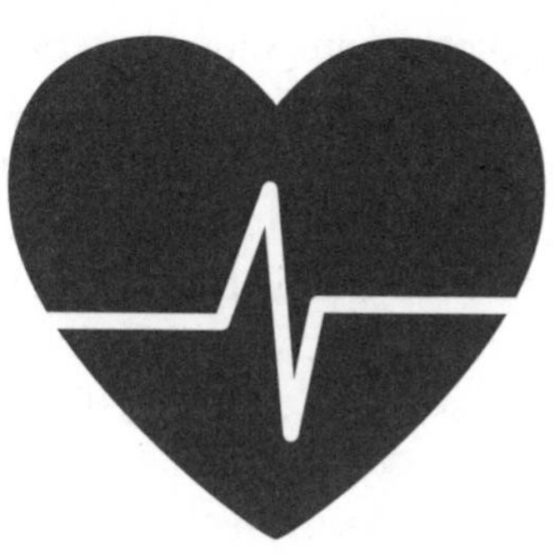

GUT FEELING

Recently, the connection between the body and the head has finally been reconnected with the emergence in mainstream media of the *microbiome*. The microbiome is the environment in our intestines. Each tiny bacterium that lives there usually has a role to play – it's almost like a little bacteria city. Those little guys make up a few pounds in weight, which is amazing when you consider how small they are. But, of course, if the gut is colonized by one type of bacteria over another, and those bacteria are pathogenic (are disease-promoting and upset the balance), they can start to have a negative impact on you, their host. You might even see an unbalanced microbiome having a negative effect on your mental health. This shows how important our gut health is, in terms of how your gut communicates with your head. It isn't even our own cells that do the communicating, it is actually the trillions of bacteria that have colonized our insides; they're in charge.

Of course, bacteria are everywhere. In the limited way we think as humans, we have a tendency to see everything in terms of black and white. Bacteria: bad. Anti-bacterial everything: good. Of course, it turns out to be just a little bit more grey, and even possibly multi-coloured. The bacteria all around us contribute to a very precious and quite fragile eco-system that inhabits us, providing all sorts of benefits, such as breaking down food and generating particular nutrients. But these guys are actually 'talking' to your head, too. You may know that the aforementioned happy hormone, serotonin, is made in huge quantities in the gut. Over 80% of serotonin is made in the gut, and you can bet your bottom dollar those little bacteria have a hand in it. Therefore, if you don't look after those little dudes (your bacteria), they will impact your behaviour, mood and life.

Of course, being human and thinking in black and white, we want a 'gut programme' or a 'microbiome programme' to **fix** us. Again, rather than separating it out, realize that there are a few gut hacks, but that a twaddle diet equals poor physical and/or mental health, and poor digestive health. Whereas a real diet, with real food, on an on-going basis, making time for yourself and your family, will result in the opposite. There is not one thing that will result in better health; it's got to be a whole-picture approach. And consistency is the key. It needs to be a less militant, and more consistent longer-term change that sticks.

Thinking on a larger scale, we should remember that we are part of a delicate ecosystem, which we need to consider in our daily actions. Essentially, humans are like one type of bacteria that have colonized this ecosystem and are causing disease to it, to our host, our wonderful planet, our home. We can keep the balance by living in harmony with our host and taking care to look after the precious plants, animals and bacteria that deliver nurturing food to us. If we don't, it will be death of the host, just like the pathogenic bacteria in our gut. If the infection is severe enough, it will be the death of us, too.

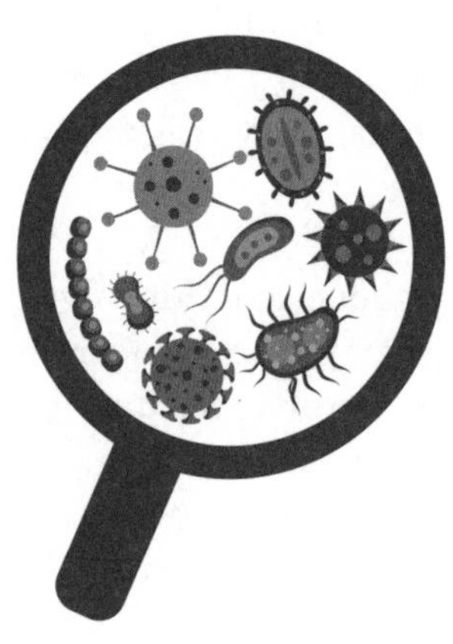

There is not one thing that will result in better health; it's got to be a whole-picture approach.

HEADLINES. GET IT? HEAD LINES

- Good head health = good body health

- Bacteria are everywhere, but our modern lifestyle and obsession with clean living ignores that these little fellows, while some cause disease (if our immunity is low or compromised), are vital for our very existence.

- There are a few bio-hacks to take our gut health to another level, but we should only use these if we can support the changes long term, and not as a fad that we drop after five minutes. In fact, in the past, eating fermented food used to be normal and not part of some mission to be perfect.

- Looking after ourselves and our microbiome extends to how we treat our environment and our planet. We can choose to ignore it but, if we want grandchildren, or even children, we'd better take the havoc we are wreaking on our soil (and oceans) seriously. Worse, this destruction by chemicals, pollutants and other toxins contributes to us living half lives – being alive, but sick as parrots.

WHY POSITIVE NUTRITION?

Nutritional science has a lot to offer us in terms of the optimization of our health. The trick is to use progressive research and apply it in our daily lives in a positive way, with amazingly positive results. It includes using micronutrient hacks to upgrade your brain, energy and focus, and looking at essential fats that act as anti-inflammatories in the body.

But the trick is also getting perspective about what the research says. Research tends to be conducted in silos – that generally means in a small isolated study that doesn't provide the big picture. One minute coffee is bad (according to the latest research) and the very next minute, it's boomeranged back into favour, because coffee drinkers are less likely to get dementia (according to the next latest research) – that is a real bit of research, by the way.

So we need to look at the big picture, while seeing what actually makes sense around food. For example, butter was bad, but now butter is back. Even when the apparent research said it was bad (who paid for the research, I wonder?). I actually never believed butter was bad anyway, because, well, it makes no sense whatsoever. We have been eating butter for thousands of years, and I never believed that margarine – a substance that doesn't go off for months, even outside the fridge, and would probably do rather better in your car engine – could possibly be good for the human body. That is just common sense. Research studies can often suffer from research bias and/or publication bias. It's more likely that the study will be published if the result has a positive outcome (and what the researcher was looking for) rather than a negative outcome, which publications might turn down for inclusion. So then that positive outcome is taken as the truth, and the negative view, of course, is never seen.

Another trend, especially as funding for university research is difficult to come by, is for corporate industry to fund research that they want conducted. Again, the research is much more likely to have the outcome that the funding is looking to support. In the 1950s, corrupt research, or at the very least misguided research, conducted by Ancel Keys, gave way to the damaging effects of sugar in the diet being underestimated and fat (of all kinds, but especially saturated fat) demonized. While Ancel Keys was right about trans-fats, it's only now that the view is swinging around to thinking that a host of other factors might contribute to heart disease.

Studies around nutrition are very difficult to conduct, as people lie in their food diaries (if the study is self reporting) and the financial reward from the research is often not enough to inspire the research in the first place.

There's no money in carrots and, unless there is a lucrative drug at the end of the rainbow, it's really difficult to fund trials that look at nutrition. Therefore, while studies are very important, never lose your own holistic view of food or this flip-flop of apparent advice will drive you crazy. The 'they', as in 'now they say coffee is good for you' doesn't care two pins for your health and well-being – so you need to take responsibility for your own health. Ask yourself: Is this real food? Did I cook it myself? Am I confident of who is selling it to me?

We should not ignore nutritional science but food is not a laboratory experiment and you are not a lab rat.

WHAT POSITIVE NUTRITION IS:

- Using cutting-edge nutritional science to our advantage for upgraded energy, good health, healing sleep and, dare I say, happiness.
- Using your common sense and getting your joy and confidence back around food.

WHAT POSITIVE NUTRITION ISN'T:

- Losing sight of our instincts around food and what actually makes sense, and eating industrialized dead or damaging food, which leaves us devoid of any nutrients that could possibly nurture us or our bodies.
- Only being interested in the short-term effects of nutrition, like getting into your new swimmers for the holiday.

We should not ignore nutritional science but food is not a laboratory experiment and you are not a lab rat.

PART 3
WHY STRATEGIC EATING?

It is a truth universally unacknowledged that most people don't actually make the connection between what they eat and how they feel.

The concept of strategic eating is that you **must** have a plan and know the rules that will guide your choices. Furthermore, the whole idea must be embedded into your very breath of life. When we eat, it's not just about being fat or thin. This is an outcome that I would encourage you to avoid, because your choice to eat strategically will result in a healthy weight and less superficial benefits besides.

The big aha is that strategic eating allows you to influence your very genetic code. This is not as fixed as you might think, but subject to the influence of the science of epigenetics. The genes and outcomes are turned on and off, in part, by the environment you bathe your tiny bodily cells in (the individual building blocks). It's really exciting stuff. The trend for genetic testing in screening DNA tests, like the '23andMe' test, are useful because they can potentially identify biochemical breaks in your system. But they are currently based on statistical probability, rather than you as an individual. You can choose to alter your eating, lifestyle and even thoughts, and potentially switch on and off the genetic outcome that these tests seem to predict. The test is like the Ghost of Christmas Yet to Come in *A Christmas Carol*. This ghosts visits Scrooge to show him the future if he doesn't change his ways. You can change your ways and influence the future, or ignore the message and think that your ill health is just down to bad luck. Getting sick can be bad luck. Ill health can result from your environment, which you may not be choosing, or something else that you can't possibly determine. Food and how you engage with food is probably the biggest influence on whether your DNA and genetic codes are switched on or off, and disease or other outcomes are the result. The wider environment is also a huge factor in how our DNA might be impaired with poor health outcomes. The more we pollute the planet's rivers and oceans, the more we risk influencing that genetic code to our detriment. We have already spectacularly caused the average fertility in men to drop dramatically over a 50-year period.

Another condition that might have an environmental root is autism. The rates were around 1 in 10,000 in the 1970s (the figures weren't monitored then, and diagnosis was poor) and are now 1 in 68 in the US as of 2018 (according to the American Autism Society). Obviously, we are a lot more aware of what autism is, but even with better diagnosis, this is a huge jump. Is it something we are doing to ourselves through our environment?

Eating strategically will allow you to upgrade yourself, potentially influencing your genetic code, and your choices influence how we curate the future of our planet. At the very least that could just mean recycling your food packaging. You don't have to go the whole hog. But we can all start.

NUTRITION NUBETTE

- Your food and shopping choices are a major player in how your genetic code could actually manifest. Do you want to leave it to bad luck? It won't be bad luck, as such. Your genetics could play out according to your environment. Yes, it is almost impossible to know which myriad factors are effecting you. The biggest player, by far, is the food choices that you make on a day-to-day basis.

TIME WAITS FOR NO MAN

However, following a plan to make good choices is a life-long experiment, and you are not perfect. You will mess up because you are for now human – that is, before the machines take over in the Tech Revolution. The important thing is to ensure that your improvement health habits are in the right direction. You are in the driver's seat, and you need to adapt your strategic eating to suit your life. No one can do that for you.

You can't expect your food choices to just happen. I urge you to recapture time, and to do so you may need to say 'No' in order to say 'Yes'. When you say yes to being at your desk all hours, you say no to making good choices in your food and lifestyle. When you choose to buy industrially farmed meat, for example, you (and it may not be consciously) say yes to pollution and the wider implications of how that might ultimately adversely affect your epigenetics. Saying no means that you choose to upgrade you and your energy, for a more stable, reliable biochemical result, for your own good certainly, but for everyone else too – no more 'H-anger' in your house or office. H-anger – hungry anger – is when your blood sugar drops and you shout at your boss. Oops.

'NINFO' (INFO) NUB

- Staying at your desk all hours of the day gives you more face time at work and makes the boss think you are a 'good egg' (nutritional reference), and that you are a 'jolly good banana' (nutritional reference), but you are sacrificing your life for time. Here's where the truth in the phrase work-life balance comes into its own.

- Being more energized and effective could enable you to be more focussed and get the work done in half the time. Go home and live life. Now there's an idea.

+ YOUR CHOICE, YOUR OUTCOME

You need an overall set of objectives, rather than just eating randomly for no particular outcome whatsoever. It's looking long term, rather than short term, and for a planned future outcome.

Long-term future outcomes might be:

- Vibrant health, even in the twilight years of life, but right now is good too.
- Kick-ass energy right now and in the future.
- Unbridled enthusiasm for life (now and for the road ahead).
- Sense of community and the concept of how more time equals happiness (yes, all this through what you eat!).
- Great health and not accepting that you have to get sick as you get older. Just don't buy that line. Even, as it turns out, with dementia.
- Being wise, not just intelligent, about choices you make for your health and your children's futures.

- Managing stress with food. Cortisol (a major stress hormone) is affected by keeping your blood sugar stable (more on that later).

- Don't accept niggling health problems – if somehow this isn't either a diet issue or a lifestyle issue (that doesn't let you process your nutrients and food to nurture you).

What would be your long-term future outcomes? What comes to mind? It doesn't have to be perfect – far be it for me to claim that I am perfect. Who wants perfection anyway?

Yes, ruin the book and jot them down right here – go and get that pencil. I'll wait!

1. ....

2. ....

3. ....

WHAT STRATEGIC EATING ISN'T

- **Short term** – going on some butt-busting diet two weeks before the holidays. Wrong book. Throw it in the bin now.
- **Worrying about your weight or calories** – as in following a celeb-based eating plan. This is about real life and real people: you.
- **Obsessed by trying to look good** – this is all about *feeling* good. Looking good is nice, but superficial. Feeling good is dynamic, leadership, contentment and meaning. It's nice to look good, but that isn't going to give you anything long term. *Feeling* good will deliver something much more amazing long term

– the energy to change you, your community and potentially your world. Now that really does matter.

- **Not enjoying food** – we all need to enjoy food. Enjoy great quality food, cooking it and, where possible, sharing it with others. Yes, there are a few guidelines, but who knows if I am right? There might be some bit on deep-digging research that tips water all over my thinking. *You* decide what makes sense. Start building your confidence and get your instincts back around what you put in your mouth. We've been doing it for millions of years. It really can't be that difficult, you would think!

WHAT STRATEGIC EATING IS

- **Long-term consciousness around eating** and noting the impact on your life (and eventually on others).
- **Making great choices moment by moment, and on occasion going off piste** (skiers know only too well what that means - a face-plant in the snow).
- **Our choices affect our epigenetics** (trigger for our genetics) and food is possibly the biggest player in how our genetics manifest.
- **Our food choices can upgrade our energy** and all those around us.
- **Having a sense of humour**, realism, and realizing that food is food and it is there to be enjoyed.

- Unless you have a very serious reason to do it (i.e., you are in seriously bad health and need to be militant), **avoid being a food faddist**. It's really boring (although that doesn't apply if you need to really pay attention to your food). The rest of us - just eat. Good choices, real food, with a few little adaptations - a few little tricks, but just eat, for goodness' sake!

- **Carving out time to create better choices**, and living rich, fruitful and happy lives.

- **Having a structure as a guide only** and designing what works best for you personally.

PART 4
STRATEGIC EATING IS STRUCTURED EATING

In effect, the strategy is the flesh on the bones, but you need a plan to get there – a skeleton to hold the whole thing up. That's the structure. You need a structure in place for success, so that you know the rules of the nutrition game. How can you possibly play any game without knowing what the rules are? The game of nutrition is no different – once you have a few marker posts in place, the rest is easy and all the confusion around food evaporates.

CREATING YOUR STRUCTURE - ENVIRONMENT

Rome wasn't built in a day – remember that your journey into nutrition is an evolving one. It's not going to be perfect from day one. Start thinking about the barriers that make it difficult for you to progress on that journey and about the small changes you can make so that your environment is more likely to support your endeavours.

KITCHEN

You don't need to have the perfect kitchen. Only spend money on the kitchen features you will use. If you don't understand the importance of making the time to prepare your own food (difficult I know – but nobody is going to do this for you), you will pay the price later. The immediate cost might not be obvious; you will feel okay. We humans are amazingly resilient in terms of how much it takes to actually kill us. We suffer a slow erosion of vitality and health. But who wants to live a half life, like some slug under a rock? Long term, nutrition and food are your investment policy in your health and how you live your life, and that all starts with how you engage in actually cooking and sourcing your food.

Here are some bits of kit that will be of essential help:

- **Blender**: I like using blenders and the best blender to buy is the one you use.

- **Sharp knives**: Invest in some great, sharp knives and a pair of industrialized scissors.

- **Saucepans**: Use ceramic frying pans – it turns out that non-stick cookware leaches chemicals into food!

- **Storage jars**: Use glass when possible for the same reason as above – certain plastics leach chemicals.

- **Great music**: I use cooking time as time for me. Listening to great music is part of that.

- **Cookbooks:** You can't beat just the classics. Even a few of the very focussed cookbooks by nutritionists are okay for inspiration, as long as you don't use them in a tense and over-the-top way. Learning to be creative around cooking comes from cooks – not nutritionists (generally) – or we would all be eating nut loaves. Nothing wrong with that, if you like nut loaves.

- **Clear kitchen surfaces**: In another life, I'd wish for more kitchen surfaces (my kitchen is really tiny, and as the house is old, I can't make it bigger)

Being "practically perfect in every way" (like Mary Poppins) is a journey of becoming more and more informed.

SHOPPING

How you shop for your food makes a huge impact on not only you and your health, but the health of your community and your planet. I try to never buy my food in a supermarket (just think of the packaging). I get everything online from a company that recycles the cardboard boxes (I just leave them out to be taken away the following week). Everything is loosely packed. I can choose one banana or ten bananas – I don't have to buy the amount of bananas determined by someone in management at the supermarket. Sometimes I buy locally, preferably from the people who produce it or are only just down the supply chain. I realize that this is a bit trickier for many city dwellers, but you can buy your produce from box schemes, even if you are an urbanite. The most well-known of these schemes is the 'Food Assembly' scheme, which is available worldwide. Local food is assembled at a local drop point, where you pick it up. Their website allows you to shop as you would from a supermarket site, but the food is all locally sourced. I know that cost is often a consideration, and far be it from me to tell you how to live your life, but despite accumulating more stuff in life (phones, cars, fancy stuff), when it comes to food, we feel that we can cut back our budget.

QUALITY

If you can afford to, upgrade to organic. Buy the best quality food you can afford. Of course, it's not always about priority, sometimes it's about reality. Affording fresh food is more expensive and it takes more effort. You might not be in a phase in your life that allows for that upgrade. But aspire to it. Eating prepared food from the supermarket might look like a no-brainer, especially when you take into account the effort involved, but prepared food is really more akin to a science experiment, rather than something that nurtures you. If you want to delve further into what is in processed food, look at Joanna Blythman's book *Swallow This*. It's an eye-opener.

Just think of the trade-off when you don't allow time to nurture yourself or your family, by staying at work until silly o'clock. Are you really going to remember that extra time you spent in the office, or those happy meals you shared with your family and children?

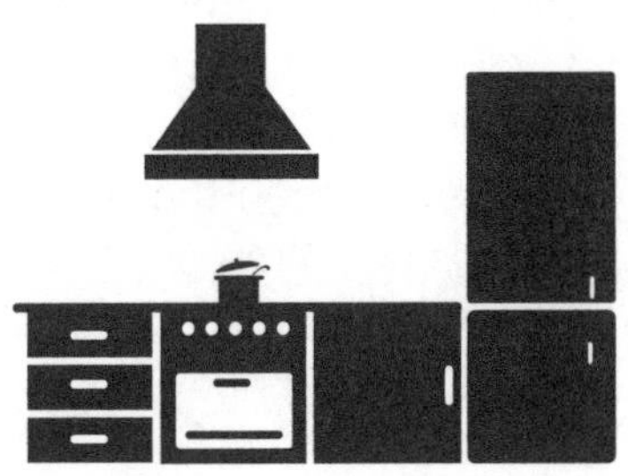

+ NUTRITION NUBETTE

- **Shop online to save time and money:** I find I pick up more stuff I don't need in a supermarket – consider a box drop scheme.

- **Recipe boxes:** I use an organic recipe box scheme for three meals in the week. This takes the aggravation out of thinking about what to cook. For those of you who haven't caught up with this trend, or if you have been living under a rock, these kind companies send you a recipe box (the one I use is fully organic) with the exact quantities required to cook a delicious meal with the instructions on how to do it. The recipes are very easy to follow, so your confidence as a cook grows. The other bit of genius is that there is obviously no waste; you only cook what you need. Compare this to going to the supermarket and being forced to buy a billion carrots rather than the one you actually need. It also saves time and money by not needing to go to the supermarket and chucking out unused food at the end of the week.

Splendid! So, in a clever way, you can actually save time and money.

- **Buy local if you can:** I go to a local organic farm. And guess what? It takes time to actually go to the farm; that elusive component of time that we need to recapture.

- **Better accounting:** I am yet to master this fully - but my theory is, if the household accounts were better run, getting better deals on your electric and/or other utilities, and paying a little more attention, then we wouldn't have to run so fast trying to earn so much money. This would then earn back time.

- **Better meal planning:** I use a menu planner (available from any good stationery shop) - look in the fridge, see what is there and create. If you are not creative, then look at Hugh Fearnley-Whittingstall's book *Love Your Leftovers*.

QUALITY OVER QUANTITY EVERY TIME

Of course, there are great cheap ingredients you can use (e.g., lentils and brown rice), but when it comes to meat (if you eat it), invest in organic if you can afford it. Mostly because of the overuse of antibiotics in farmed animals, which will have an impact on your immunity and microbiome. As for vegetables, pesticide use - especially a class of chemical known as glyphosate - affects your gut microbiome by killing gut bacteria. Glyphosate specifically affects the bacteria by shutting down the shikimate pathway in bacteria. As humans aren't directly affected by this biochemical pathway, this mechanism has been underplayed, ignoring the fact that, while we aren't killed, our tiny friends in our guts are. As it turns out, the guys in our guts (the microbiome) are vital for our health. Killing them has a drastic effect on our own health, and is thought to contribute to auto-immune diseases.

It's important to make these changes in stages. Being "practically perfect in every way" (like Mary Poppins) is a journey of becoming more and more informed. Do your research and see where you feel happy starting. But don't ignore making these changes because you are too busy. Do something, however small it may be, but do it!

COOKING

This is a tricky one. In historical terms, the actual day-to-day cooking and/or food nurturing was traditionally done by women, until around the 1970s (in the UK). Women discovered their economic power around this time. It seemed that the payoff between slaving away in front of a hot stove, as in the old ways, was not worth returning to when you could easily bring in a pre-packaged gourmet version into the microwave. Who can blame us? Especially after a long day in the office. Why shouldn't we? As more of us have abandoned the kitchen for the workplace, tumbleweeds, bats, and cobwebs are where the cook used to be in residence. I am not saying that it should be women who refill the post, but someone has to do it. And if you do want vibrant health, cooking is a big part of it.

- Can you share the cooking with another member of the family?

- Are your children old enough that you can teach them a few recipes and let them get on with it?

- Can you make a rota to divide this responsibility up fairly?

TIME

Time is created by having stunning, all-day energy by eating better – which creates time to purchase stunning food and prepare it.

- **Love the slow cooker** – just throw everything in and switch it on for a hot evening meal. It is that easy.

PLANNING

For low-tech planning, get a menu planner. You need to plan your food intake like you would a project at work. You wouldn't expect a project at work to happen by accident, and food in the fridge doesn't happen by accident, either.

Most cooking, and the basis of any recipe, can be made with these basic ingredients:

- Onions
- Garlic, herbs and spices
- Tomatoes (I'll even settle for tinned)
- Vegetables
- Basic protein if you eat fish or meat; otherwise, feta cheese and eggs are all good substitutes for vegetarians
- Olive oil

Stocking your fridge is a bit like a capsule wardrobe. You take your basics, and then mix and match with what you have.

Eating brilliant food will have an impact on all areas of your life, not least on how well you sleep.

FAMILY

A great anxiety for the modern family is providing food for everyone, since it's likely that each member eats a different meal and at different times.

For example, my daughter is a fusspot, but I get her to try food every time I cook it. She has to try it 14 times before she can decide that she genuinely does not like it. I got that from a TV programme on food psychology – so I am sticking with it, although I don't know if it is based in scientific fact or not. Children's taste buds change and develop, so don't give up. Eating as a family is also vital so they don't see eating as something separate and functional (just refuelling).

Children are developing eating disorders earlier and earlier, as they become more and more paranoid, while still going for masses of dietary twaddle (i.e., junk food). While they learn about food technology in school, they are bound to be confused. Who had the idea to industrialize how we learn about food? Genius.

If possible, try to:

- Eat together as a family if you can – yes, it's more of an effort.

- Eat breakfast together; more on that shortly.

- Eating together is a great opportunity to teach children how to interact and do that old fashioned thing – have a conversation.

- Food eaten out of packet, while standing at the counter, is a bit sad. Even if it's you by yourself, sit down at the table. I expect nothing less than black tie and napkins.

- Eat mindfully. No devices. No excuses. It's really not that urgent. RESIST.

WORK HOURS

Eating brilliant food will have an impact on all areas of your life, not least on how well you sleep. So with the demands of long hours at work, a healthy diet will provide you with a new found energy to get in early after a great night's shuteye.

You need to:

- Create some boundaries at work, so that food isn't just fuel and your last priority.

- Get the food planning done, so you know what you are going to eat.

- Cook up some extra (stew or whatever) and freeze it – so that when it all goes horribly wrong, you know you have something ready to go.

- Don't eat too late – it's much better to have a good lunch and have something really light for dinner, if this is an unavoidable pattern.

FREEZING

I freeze lots of stuff. I buy packs of fish, sustainable, of course, not farmed, or a frozen organic chicken or meat. Then I have to look at my plan and see what I am meant to be doing. Of course, sometimes it all goes horribly wrong. Sometimes the planning thing works for months, and sometimes I am hopeless. I never give up thinking that I will finally crack it, and everything in my household and life will work like a well-oiled machine.

Preparing food on the weekend can be a bore, but spend just one hour thinking about what could help you during the week ahead.

A favourite snack of mine is homemade roasted almonds. Just throw some whole organic almonds in some water and soak for four hours. Then drain the almonds and pat them dry with kitchen paper. Tip the almonds onto a baking tray with a drizzle of olive oil and some lemon juice and a little salt, if you like. Put into a preheated oven (150 °c) for about an hour and don't let them burn.

Stews are good for weekend prep, especially easy using a slow cooker. Or with conventional cooking: In a pan, brown some meat or chicken in a little olive oil. Take it out of the pan and place it on a plate. Then sizzle some chopped onions in a pan with a little bit of olive oil*, and add some chopped celery and carrots. When the vegetables soften, add the meat (or lentils or chickpeas if you are vegetarian) and some stock (a good quality stock cube would be fine). If you have a bay leaf, put that in. You could use a tomato base; use organic if you can, but don't get too hung up on the details. Leave the stew to cook for a couple hours.

NOTE: Don't get samey about cooking.

(*People get hot under the collar about the cooking temperatures of oil, which can be ruined and denatured by heat. Essentially, you should never cook with sunflower/ hemp or vegetable oil (whatever the recipe says). Cooking with olive oil is ok. If you have to cook at very high temperatures, use coconut oil (you can get a good organic one that doesn't taste of coconuts).

PART 5
CREATING YOUR STRATEGY

In order to play the strategic game of nutrition to its fullest, you'll need a few pointers as to the rules of the game. Let's use some general principles as a foundation, then we can consider some guidelines to follow, with a few upgrades for those who are already doing the basics. If you are starting with the basics then, in time, you can aim for the upgrade – but remember, you don't have to be perfect right from the start. That's fad thinking.

In order to have pots of energy and a long-term path to vibrant health, you need to understand and use the following strategies – each of which will be explored further in the next sections. These strategies will help you if you are new to all things nutrition by starting at the 'Base Camp' section. If you are a bit more comfortable, then incorporate a few changes that are shared in 'Camp 1', or if you are already doing all those, then go to the 'Summit'. You'll get the picture.

Remember,
you don't have
to be perfect
right from
the start.

SUMMARY OF THE STRATEGIES COVERED

1. **Blood sugar management:** This explores how your body handles glucose in your blood, so that you have stable and consistent energy all day, without missing a beat. Blood sugar management is the most important concept to understand. The thinking is that nearly every poor health outcome has to do with insulin, which is an important hormone in balancing other hormones and blood sugar.

2. **Inflammation:** Inflammation is the root of many industrialized diseases, which by and large could be avoided if we made better ongoing food choices. It really is easy to avoid inflammatory foods once you know the rules on this one.

3. **Focus on the outcomes:** Here's where focussing on the details is important. If you are in poor health for whatever reason, get it sorted. Don't believe you are powerless. Even if you improve your health slightly, that is progress. So while I've said not to be a militant eating

fusspot, sometimes you have to pay a little more attention to the details.

4. **Look after the little things:** Look after the powerhouses of your cells - your mitochondria. These are organelles that produce all the energy in your body (adenosine triphosphate - ATP). If these guys are not firing, you won't be, either.

   We are living indoors, out of natural sunlight, compromising our vitamin D levels, causing ourselves all sorts of problems, not least for our immune systems.

5. **Focus on quality:** This is important for your nutrient levels and also supports real farming rather than food manufacturing. Eating real food is extremely important, vital in fact. However, due to poor farming methods and food distribution, even seemingly fresh food can be stored for months before we eat it, and so the quality of the nutrients in the food can be denatured. Eating real food is great, but let's not ignore nutritional science altogether - let's not lose sight of *food* at the base of everything, rather than reductionist nutrients alone.

6. **Fat can be our friend:** As it turns out, white twaddle carbohydrates are not our best buddy. Twaddle carbohydrates include buns, cake, donuts, white bread, white rice, white and fluffy food. But it's important to make sure that we have the type of fat that our bodies are designed to run on.

7. **Food fad or real life:** It seems that everybody has either a gluten or dairy intolerance these days. It turns out that our Western lifestyle can lead to inflammation. These foods (and the way they are farmed) can result in inflammation. What can we do? Could looking after our little friends in our gut help? What about fasting regimes (like the 5:2)? Coffee and butter? Yuck or good?

8. **Reconnect with your body:** Your body is what processes the nutrients you get from your food. If you run your body at full tilt, burning the candle at both ends, you are stressed, you don't get enough sleep, or you expose yourself to stuff that your mitochondria (those little powerhouses) can't handle, then there's 'trouble at mill' with your health. There is no getting around it. I remember a friend of mine saying that there was no point doing the nutrition thing, because the beauty editor

of some fashion magazine had been crazed about eating the right diet, but had died anyway. Yes, that is unfortunate, obviously, but we don't know what else might have been affecting her health. Stress? Environment? Sleep? Even our personality and character affect our health. Of course, exercise fits in to this section. Exercise is not especially good at burning off calories, but it is marvellous for all sorts of other things, not least for the transport of nutrients around the body.

9. **Reconnect with your food:** We have become so accustomed to buying packs of nutritionally void food, or stuffing our food in our mouths while walking and multi-tasking. This principle puts food back on the table and makes it central to your life.

10. **Reconnect with people via food and create communities through food - even if that is with your own family:** Reconnect with your world and environment. This might be ambitious, but can we reconnect with our community via food? Can we find meaning in food beyond food as a fuel? How might nutrition positively give us a wholeness and meaning that we can't even imagine? Yes, I said it was ambitious.

STRATEGY 1: BLOOD SUGAR MANAGEMENT

This is the foundation of what you must understand about how nutrition contributes to great energy. It matters a bit less what particular dietary system you have chosen to follow (i.e., paleo or vegan), but whatever you believe nurtures you personally, you fundamentally must have stable energy and be full enough so that you are not always reaching into the biscuit tin or toffee jar.

What follows is the short and nontechnical version of how blood sugar management works. If you want more information on the biochemical explanation, a good book is *The Blood Sugar Solution*, by Mark Hyman. It's also written for the layman.

Our body allows for about a teaspoon of glucose to circulate in our bodies at any one time. Glucose is vital, because it is the fuel we require to power our bodily machine – us! However, too much of a good thing isn't necessarily wonderful. It is a very delicate balance – almost a conjuring trick. The point is, our biochemistry works on very fine margins and, although we may not feel it, our systems are constantly trying to achieve something called homeostasis, which means that our biochemistry is trying to achieve balance and order. In order to do this, there are literally hundreds of biochemical reactions involved, often working on complicated feedback mechanisms. The principal hormone involved in the maintenance of blood sugar is insulin. Insulin lowers blood sugar by opening the cells, like a key in a lock, and allowing the glucose to enter the cell. The cells use glucose to produce energy -adenosine triphosphate or ATP.

Insulin is also a fat storage hormone. When blood sugar is too low, we rely on stored glucose (glycogen) found in the liver and the muscles, which help balance this very delicate equation. The big issue with our modern diet is that we are either eating the whole day, and triggering insulin the whole day, or we are eating food that our ancestors couldn't even imagine in their wildest dreams (or nightmares). Lots of white, fluffy carbohydrates and sugar. Whenever we want it. Our bodies are designed to collect food in a time of plenty for the moment when there will be a lean time or famine. The way we collect and store food is as fat. In our modern age, the lean time never comes – it's party time, all the time.

Although we have moved on in our mental intelligence – we have the ability to reach the stars, Mars and beyond – we are still just those fat-storing apes, remember? Unfortunately, we are nothing more glamorous than that. Chubby chimps. We would rather take the short-term, addictive shortcut of stuffing our faces with the aforementioned twaddle, because in the short term we love the temporary high from the sugar (or white carb) fix. We are addicted. We are biochemically programmed to go for the food that will store the best, so that in lean times we can live off our fat.

The short version of understanding what to eat is:

The brainy professors came up with a system called the glycaemic index (GI) and then a more complicated glycaemic load, which ranks foods on how quickly they burn in the body. A high GI food would be something like mashed potatoes, because there is no processing for the body to do. A lower GI food would be lentils, for example, as there is quite a bit of processing to do in the body. It's about how quickly the sugar from the food raises your blood sugar. A lot depends on the density of the food – so the denser the food, the lower the GI (and the better). Although this has obvious faults, I am going to summarize below.

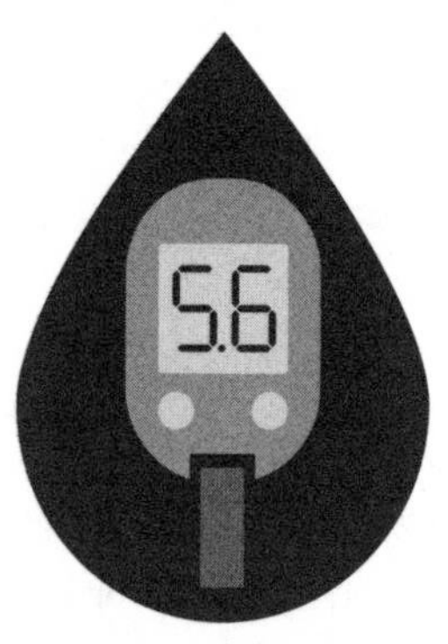

As real live
bodies,
our system
continually
adapts to
its environment.

QUICK BLOOD SUGAR GUIDE FOR DUMMIES

Sweet, fluffy and white foods will tend to raise and drop your blood sugar. Sweet is anything that tastes sweet and fluffy is the density of the food. Fluffy things are light, like candy floss or rice cakes, and processed things like mashed potatoes. They look fluffy, don't they? White food has been processed (i.e., an apple danish). Candy floss (which our American cousins call cotton candy) is very sweet, fluffy and would be white if it wasn't dyed pink with some toxic dye. It's sweet, fluffy and white. Remember that mashed potato? Fluffy and white.

So, you are aiming for food that balances the blood sugar – real food, but specifically thick fibrous protein and fat, or dense or chewy food. When you do the chewing, the amount of sugar that is released into the blood is done slowly. When you buy ready-made food, it is already pre-processed, and might spike the blood sugar if it is hyper-processed. Grub in its natural state, food you have to chew and that's fibrous, is what you should be adding to your daily food intake. It's food that might still have a skin. It hasn't had its nutritional soul stripped out.

Also, make sure you have some protein at every meal (you don't need vast amounts, like a huge steak). Nuts are protein, for example, so a small handful of nuts will help balance blood sugar.

We have all become massively fat phobic, mostly because of the calorie argument (fat is calorific), but when we look at the biochemistry, it turns out the body is not like Stevenson's Rocket, the famous steam engine. We don't have a boiler that we need to constantly stuff and stoke with coal (fuel) to make it go. We experience entropy, which is a loss of heat through our open systems (our bodies). The calorie argument centres around the laws of thermodynamics, which is fine if we were actually machines, but we aren't. The laws of thermodynamics don't determine how we lose or store weight; they never have.

It's about energy. We have all sorts of clever bits, like our digestive systems and livers that metabolize fat, and food generally. As real live bodies, our system continually adapts to its environment. It turns out when food is scarce after initial weight loss, we will start to store weight. Ancel Keys, remember him? He found this out in an experiment conducted at the end of the Second World War – the famous Minnesota Starvation Experiment in 1945. After the volunteers lost weight at the beginning of the experiment, their weight plateaued and, once they started eating normally again, they then stored more weight than they had to begin with. Every dieter's song.

In all the work Ancel Keys did around fat (i.e., demonizing it) he was right about one thing – trans-fat (which used to be found in all processed food) is not good for the body. The body struggles to recognize it. The food industry has acknowledged this and has removed it from most products. However, this doesn't mean that something equally as harmful hasn't taken its place – we are yet to find out. Fat or fatty food that used to be demonized – like butter, avocados, nuts, coconut fat and lard – are all suddenly back in fashion. Just watch the flip-flop on the nutritional pendulum on that one. It's about steering a steady and middle route as opposed to veering in one nutritional direction and back again.

ONE MORE TRICK

Add fat (so called good fat – i.e., avocado, coconut, butter, olives and olive oil, coconut fat, salmon, fresh walnuts), protein or fibre if you want to stabilize the blood sugar further. So, if you eat an apple with some almonds and half an avocado, that will keep the blood sugar stable, you will feel full and satisfied, and your energy will be very constant (without dips, fluctuations, or feeling either hungry (h-angry) or tired). Magic.

GLYCAEMIC INDEX – THE SHORTCOMINGS

There are a few obvious problems with this system. Food burns differently in different people. Good or poor blood sugar control depends on numerous factors that are unique to the person eating the food.

How does their digestive system process the food? Do they have the right nutrients to process the food (like chromium and zinc), do they chew their food? Are they actually insulin resistant (so the hormone doesn't work very well at a cellular level)?

The broad GI guidelines also ignore the effects of fructose (a type of sugar that has a very low GI, but isn't good in excess and can cause the liver to store fat), which are so much of the root cause of obesity.

The Quick Blood Sugar Guide is not perfect, but used as a rule of thumb, it helps you choose foods that are most likely to keep the blood sugar stable, in theory.

- Choose real food and don't go for processed food.

- Eat some protein and some good quality fat at each meal. Remember, good fat might be avocado, butter, coconut oil or nuts.

- A sausage will balance the blood sugar (because of the protein and fat), but obviously a sausage is not a healthy product – not least because the meat might be of an uncertain provenance and have all sorts of other stuff chucked in.

NUTRITION NUBETTE

Balance the blood sugar right from the beginning of the day by eating a fabulous breakfast. If you don't get this bit right, the blood sugar wobbles for the rest of the day. This is tip number one. A fabulous breakfast might be:

1. Eggs, any which way for breakfast is a good standby.

2. Rye toast (nice and dense) with nut butters (protein), like almond nut butters.

   For example: Eggs and avocado will do a champion job of balancing the blood sugar. A yummy breakfast that will really keep you full.

3. Smoothie: I like using kefir, a specific yogurt drink (more on that later), yogurt, and a little frozen fruit for taste.

4. Super green smoothie - Just so long as it fits in with your life and you are not doing it for faddy reasons. If you are being faddy, it's probably your life you need to change first (too much stress, not enough time).

BASE CAMP

You are just at the starting point of upgrading your energy. So, to get the best from optimal blood sugar balance:

1. Eat breakfast (see the ideas above) - don't eat a muffin at your desk. That is just sad and a disaster for blood sugar control. If you eat a twaddle breakfast, you will feel hungrier than if you had skipped breakfast.

2. Eat breakfast at home if possible - remember to avoid sweet, fluffy and white stuff. So don't have cereal unless it's oats, and they're good quality, and then add nuts (protein). Just get breakfast achieved. Don't worry about all the other details yet. Breakfast eaten together as a family can be done, honestly. At least eat at the table, if you can't face anyone else.

CAMP 1

You eat breakfast and you want an upgrade.

1. Eat real food that you have to cook yourself and expand that to other meals.

2. Don't eat commercial bread, even if it says it's healthy. Most commercial breads are made by the Chorley Wood Bread Processing Method. This means that it may contain all sorts of ingredients that you might not expect have been added (like sugar). Brown commercial bread is often dyed brown with caramel. Don't be fooled.

3. Preferably go for the savoury breakfast - goat cheese, eggs, fish (sardines, even canned ones, are great if that's your breakfast preference).

SUMMIT

Your blood sugar is balanced.

How do you know? Your energy throughout the day is stable – you are not getting dips in energy. You are not craving food. You are not losing your rag or feeling shaky if your food is a little late. Your hormones are in tune. You haven't shouted at your kids, your spouse or your boss for quite a while. Your sleep is deep and restful, and you are not waking up in the night. You don't have a tummy-tire. Tummy-tires bulge when insulin is being produced to try to balance the blood sugar, usually when the insulin response is being over triggered. So constant eating, or eating the sweet, fluffy and white stuff, makes the hormones work harder. Insulin is then encouraging the body to store the excess sugar in the blood as fat near the liver.

1. If your blood sugar is stable, experiment with pushing breakfast a little later. This will extend the period of your overnight fast. Only do this if all the above criteria are met and you are eating real food as a baseline. There are all sorts of benefits to doing this, which we will come to later.

2. Think about replacing the later breakfast with a kefir smoothie or green smoothie. Put an avocado in for fat, with the kefir as the protein or use a nut protein powder (or similar). Throw in what you have: cucumber, parsley, a few rocket leaves, an apple, baby spinach and a bit of water. Don't use raw kale because of the oxalic acid, which makes some nutrients difficult to absorb. Raw spinach has the same problem, but most experts agree that stomach acid can deal with the more mulchy spinach leaves. Also, remember that doing the same thing every day (like having a kale smoothie) is probably not ideal, but that type of moderation applies to a lot of things.

3. Consider making flaxseed crackers – get one cup of brown linseed (flax), half a cup of ground almonds, two tablespoons of chia seeds (if you must), some herbs and a little pinch of chilli flakes. Add half a cup of water. Press the dough flat onto a baking tray (like a big thin biscuit) and bake at 150°c for about 50 minutes. These are a lifesaver if you're feeling peckish. Remember, this is the fancy footwork – get the basics in first.

STRATEGY 2: CONQUERING INFLAMMATION

Our ancient relatives had an advantage – when they swung down from the trees all those years ago, those with more ability to create inflammation had an evolutionary advantage. The Apo4 gene marker creates inflammation in our bodies, and those that had this genetic gene pool were destined to pass on this useful marker to the next generation. Inflammation is necessary. It helps heal injury, which was great if you were out walking and cut your foot (no shoes in those days, you see). But it's not so great nowadays, as you're sitting at your desk at work and doing battle with the great Excel or Word tribe.

Inflammation is the underlying cause of nearly all degenerative diseases, from Alzheimer's to cancer and a few things in between (like arthritis). It's your diet that can contribute to a huge hunk of this inflammation (or not). It's not rocket science – eating a diet full of anti-inflammatory foods, such as fruits and vegetables, is a great start. They contain all sorts of phyto (plant) chemicals that make that happen. Eating twaddle food (e.g., commercial cereal and pro-inflammatory foods, which don't have those magic phytochemicals in them), creates inflammation. Added to that, twaddle food tends to be higher in an inflammatory type of essential fat called Omega 6, found in baked goods and cereal products. Omega 6 fats are essential; the problem is that we have far too much of it in our diets, and usually the fat has been processed and denatured within an inch of its life. We need Omega 3 fats, which are found mainly in oily fish (the smaller fish that are less contaminated) and in a few other foods like walnuts. But fish is the biggest hit by far. The ratio of Omega 6 to Omega 3 consumption might be as high as 17:1 - of course, there is a lot of debate about the ideal ratio. Some anthropological analysis says that the ratio should ideally be 1:1.

If you have health problems like irritable bowel syndrome (IBS) or other digestive problems, you should consider dairy as a contributor. The industrially produced milk that we drink in North America and Europe is from a certain breed of cow, which produces A1 milk, and this contains a protein that doesn't get on with our guts. You could experiment with milk from other types of cows; for instance, a high proportion of Guernsey cows produce A2 milk. The protein A1 particularly stimulates inflammation. And some people have other problems with how they actually break down and digest the milk; they lack the enzymes to break the proteins down effectively. Yet another issue is the sheer volume of milk we can crack through in the cappuccino society. Others worry about the impact of hormones in the milk, which might also play havoc with our own biochemistry.

+ NUTRITION NUBETTE

- If milk doesn't agree with you, avoid it. You may feel bloated, need to use the bathroom frequently, have skin complaints (like eczema) or brain fog. Don't wait for an expert to tell you this. If you avoid milk and you feel better, go with that.

- Some people find the protein in goat's and sheep's milk easier to digest. Soft sheep's cheese doesn't sound lovely, but it really is. Try soft sheep's cheese with some plums, as an after-dinner vibe. Seriously yum.

- If milk doesn't seem to cause a problem, dairy that has been turned into other products through bacterial action, like yogurt, might be a better choice and easier on digestion.

- Go organic whenever possible. You only have to visit an organic farm to know that it is the right and humane thing to do.

- Some cheeses actually appear to help the microbiome (remember, those guys in your gut).

- Some swear by raw milk. Raw milk is available straight from the farm. Make sure it's organic. Obviously, it is teeming with bacteria, so storing it in the fridge is a must. Raw milk would be a public health issue if it were available in shops, and the distribution channels would make that impossible. But, I promise you, there is nothing quite as delicious as raw milk (again, I am lucky to have a local farm that I can order raw milk from). Thanks, Goodwood Home Farm.

+

A NUTRITION NUBETTE ON SUGAR

I am sure you know that sugar isn't really a healthy product. Of course, a little of what you fancy might do you good, but we have gone totally potty for the sweet stuff. Most experts agree that our food consumption has skyrocketed from an estimate of 12 pounds a year at the beginning of the 19th century to 47 pounds per person by the end. So, is the continuing debate and pussy-footing around sugar actually fuelled by the food industry? Dr Robert Lustig has studied the apparent addictive quality of sugar and he has the data to substantiate his claims - of course, it isn't just him. The sugar industry denies that it is addictive. If it is addictive, then surely it should be controlled, like drugs and alcohol!

In 1931, the brilliant German biochemist Otto Warburg won a Nobel Prize for discovering how cells respire. Excess glucose causes the cells to breathe without oxygen. We know that this pathway feeds cancer. At the very least, if your health isn't good, it can exacerbate yeasty overgrowth in the body. The World Health Organization (WHO) says we should aim for no more than six teaspoons of added sugar. There was a lot of pressure from the sugar industry, together with some veiled threats to withdraw the US funding contribution to the WHO. This six teaspoon figure is probably a compromise, I suspect. How did they come up with this number; it really doesn't sound very scientific. Even if you don't reassess sugar for yourself, look at the toxic effect on the environment.

Sugar sucks water, and the by-products are toxic and contribute to soil erosion. Stripping our planet's resources is quite simply unsustainable. But you can make a difference by making different choices.

SUGAR NUBETTE

- Twaddle food is where a lot of sugar lurks without you realizing it.
- Sucrose is table sugar - not good for all the reasons above.
- Sugar messes with the mitochondria - in excess, it causes overload and stops these tiny energy plants from working effectively.
- Fructose is found in fruit, which is OK if you eat the whole fruit because real fruit has sufficient fibre to slow down how fast the body processes it. However fruit juices (which are processed fruit) contribute to non-alcoholic fatty liver disease and weight gain. Avoid whenever possible. Giving fruit juice to a child is like giving them alcohol (without making them drunk - but it has the same metabolic effect).
- You are not a monk (or maybe you are?), so occasionally a little tiny something sweet makes the world go around. Don't go mad and it's not an excuse - again, great quality dark chocolate,

why not? But a bowl of twaddle commercial cereal is just addiction.

- Alternatives to sugar are marketed with health benefits – I am sure that something will be found why that isn't a good idea (i.e., Xylitol affects the friendly bacteria and can result in loose stools, and I am sure there will be a problem with all those sugar substitutes somewhere down the line). A bit of maple syrup (a dribble) or a smidge of raw local honey (quality again) can be a good alternative.

- If you feel that you are craving sugar, it's probably your blood sugar, so go back to getting some nutritional basics in. Get your blood sugar stable, and that sweet tooth will disappear. Feeding the bacteria in the gut with real food, which will balance the gut, is key. Start balancing the blood sugar by eating the right breakfast.

- If you really can't quit the sugar devil, then maybe you are yeasty, which will make you crave sugar. Yeast means that your system has tipped into an unbalanced state, and more yeast is able to grow in the gut or elsewhere. Go to a nutritional therapist and work out a plan.

ALCOHOL NUBETTE

Alcohol isn't a healthy product. Although a few studies show that red wine might have some benefits (but since it has been muted that the amount of resveratrol – the chemical compound thought to be beneficial – would be too massive to fit into a bottle of wine). Some studies show that moderate drinking improves longevity, but it might be the other activities that go around drinking that contribute to that, like enjoying time with friends and having a drink, rather than the other way around.

- Choose quality, especially with wine, which has all sorts of undeclared processing aids in it, including milk and eggs – I buy organic, non-sulphite wine where possible.

- Vodka and soda with lime? Remember that vodka is 40% proof (minimum), so not ideal for the liver.

- Beers tend to be very yeasty, and cider very sugary, but choose your moment and choose quality.

Get back to nurturing and replenishing your gut, which starts with food.

CAFFEINE NUBETTE

Some studies show that coffee guards against cognitive decline and helps prevent Alzheimer's. Apparently, coffee the wonder drug might even prevent bowel cancer, according to the experts. You can't get away from the fact that coffee has a stimulant in it and can make you jittery. Coffee also is a digestive stimulant, so it can help in the bathroom department. On the other hand, in excess it can contribute to fibrocystic breast disease (FBD), although the experts can't agree on that, either. I can tell you that it was true for me - I lived in Italy in my 20s and developed FBD, but as soon as I quit coffee, it went away - coincidence? But studies are very difficult to conduct on food and habit (what coffee was used in any study), and it's reductionist.

The amount of coffee we are drinking of iffy quality, and the quantity of industrially produced milk we use with it, might not be a good thing. One lovely thoughtful cup, which makes your heart sing, might be just lovely. It might really be the dose that makes the poison, to paraphrase Paracelsus.

A WORD ON ALLERGY/INTOLERANCE

These days, it seems that everyone either is or thinks they are allergic to something. This isn't our imagination. From the perspective of being a nutritional therapist (working holistically), this is all getting to be a problem. Where I would start as a nutritional therapist is to repair and nourish the gut. So, if you know a food is bothering you, it's silly to eat it and make it worse (the key offenders are wheat, dairy, gluten, soy and many more that apply individually). I have a friend who is allergic to lettuce and cucumber! But it is always worth going to a nutritional therapist – a recommendation works best, although you can look up the British Association for Nutrition and Applied Nutritional Therapy (BANT) and find someone local.

Why have humans become more and more sensitive to food? Plenty of reasons: pesticides on food, especially glyphosates, rushed eating, too much twaddle food (especially cheap wheat and gluten products), less resilient systems generally, less fibrous diet, stress, city living, eating and living too clean – basically being alive in the 21st century. But, don't despair, you can live a healthy life by trying to get to the root of your problem, rather than just eliminating foods (necessary in the short term, obviously). Get back to nurturing and replenishing your gut, which starts with food. Avoiding wheat and dairy is a good place to start to avoid the symptoms, but ultimately you must get to the root cause for you. Is it stress? Is it your bacterial mix? Is it something pathogenic (i.e., something causing symptoms, like a parasite)? Find out and get it sorted.

A NUBBETTE ON VEGETABLES

Eat more vegetables than fruits. In some countries, the governmental advice is nine a day (it used to be the five a day in the UK, which of course got hijacked by the food marketers). But even if it were five a day, aim for a ratio of four bits of vegetables to one bit of fruit.

Remember, too, that certain fruits and vegetables are much more widely treated with pesticides than others. As a rule of thumb, soft fruits, herbs, and pre-packaged salad are among the worst. Grain is also widely sprayed (wheat particularly), so go for organic.

BASE CAMP

1. Eat real food. Yes, that is always the basic advice. So getting organized is the key on that one. Plenty of fruits and vegetables, organic if you can. Remember that in the US, only 7% of available family income is spent on food; in the UK it is 9% and in Australia 11%. There has got to be some scope to change that percentage. Can we make good food a priority over more and more other stuff?

2. Consider taking a krill oil supplement (krill are what the fish eat to get their omega 3s).

3. Consider eating spelt bread (a more ancient type of wheat) and other grains instead of wheat. Spelt has less gluten. Gluten is thought by most nutritionists to contribute to inflammation (and to autoimmune issues). Modern wheat is really a problem, as it has a higher gluten content.

CAMP 1

1. All of the above.

2. Consider cutting out wheat. Yes, I know that sounds really faddy, but most wheat products are made like industrial products and are not actually real food. Non-organic wheat has higher glyphosate residues, which is a naughty pesticide. You could replace this with organic spelt, but eliminating forces you to look for other choices, like organic rye (the gluten is a slightly different chemical structure) and tends to be manufactured better.

3. Eat more little oily fish – at least three times a week (as above).

4. Take the krill supplement if you are deficient. Go to the optician and ask them if you are deficient. They can tell (apparently) by looking at your tear ducts and how dry your eyes are. You could take a functional medicine test, but unless your health is in a bad way, you don't have to go into that kind of detail.

5. Inflammatory lifestyle – breathing exercises (just breathe in for four counts, hold for four counts and breathe out for six counts). Holding the breath changes the CO_2 ratio (CO_2 is acidic, over-acidity is inflammatory). Stress is inflammatory! Get some lavender essential oil, a calming oil (or one of those diffusers).

SUMMIT

1. Make sure you are doing all of the above – real food, that old one again!

2. Watch sugar, especially as it contributes to the Maillard reaction in the body. This is a reaction that basically toasts (browns) your cells and ages them.

3. Replace gluten products with other non-gluten bases. The gluten grains are BROW – barley, rye, oats and wheat. Aim for sweet potatoes, rice (brown, white and wild), buckwheat and quinoa.

4. This upgrade is only if you are suffering from inflammation (i.e., have something you need to attend to in your health). Lectins in some foods have an inflammatory component (lectins are a type of protein). I believe that if you occasionally eat inflammatory food, it might even have a mildly positive effect (but not if you are already sick). Avoiding lectins is especially relevant if you have an autoimmune condition. Foods high in lectins are beans, pulses, grains and cereal. There are loads of fruits and vegetables that also have lectins – only look at this micro detail if you have tried everything else. You may want to seek expert help.

5. The fibre you find in fruits and vegetables is naturally anti-inflammatory.

6. Upgrade: it's nine fruits and vegetables a day – you can throw them in the super green smoothie. It does denature the fibre slightly, but don't worry too much, just do it!

7. Eat plenty of garlic, onions and leeks (high in alliums – another component of some foods) and crucifers such as broccoli, cabbage, cauliflower, mustard greens and Brussels sprouts. These are also sulphur foods, thought to be very low in the modern diet. These foods are high in anti-oxidants. That means instead of rusting like an old car, these elements protect you and your cells.

Eat real food. Yes, that is always the basic advice.

STRATEGY 3: FOCUS ON YOUR BODY, YOUR HEALTH AND THE OUTCOMES

If you suffer from poor health, get it fixed. Don't suffer. Of course, there are times when that warrants a trip to the doctor's surgery, and this is certainly the place to go if you have any serious worries about your health. The problem comes when the only solution is a pill for every ailment, and there appears to be no real solution to your problem except another pill to stop the side effect of the last one. Poor health isn't caused by a deficiency in prescriptions.

Niggly health problems – like digestive troubles, minor stress issues, mild depression or anxiety, and feeling tired – can only really be solved by *you*. First steps: blood sugar control, avoid twaddle food, go for real food and cut the sugar. If your health is compromised, it's time to focus on the details until it's fixed.

- If the problem is serious (or you are worried), go to the doctor.

- If they send you away without a real solution, take matters into your own hands. Get to the root cause of the issue. Address your diet and how you are living your life.

- Making a change is going to take a bit of effort – exercise, relaxation, food and sleep.

- Just think about how you might treat a favourite pet; you know they have needs – exercise, play and good food – so treat yourself with the same loving kindness.

An emerging medical field is Functional Medicine, where biochemical tests are used to determine breaks in function. If you are feeling tired and cold and gaining weight, the doctor might diagnose thyroid issues and put you on medication (and of course, sometimes it can be dangerous not to follow the advice of your doctor). In functional medicine, the practitioner might be looking for why the thyroid is not working, looking at stress hormones like cortisol, or nutrient deficiencies like iodine. But it is important to find the root cause of such issues, and you should obviously go to your doctor, but remember there might be a lot you can contribute to your own health by taking action. Getting a natural health practitioner to help you on your journey can be very helpful.

LOOK AFTER YOUR GUT

Don't tolerate gut issues. Problems you might experience include bloating, gas, running to the loo, constipation or gripes. The gut is the foundation to great health. Apparently, Confucius said, "Bliss begins in the bowel," and who are we to disagree?

Sorting out the gut is important and the basis for good health. Here are some suggestions for you to consider. But always see a qualified professional to help you identify what specifically applies to you.

- **Try avoiding wheat** – replace it with rye, barley oats, rice, buckwheat, polenta or other substitutes. As mentioned earlier, wheat, especially in commercial products, affects our digestion.

- **Try avoiding dairy** – You might be OK with yogurt or kefir (although dairy, they are processed by bacteria and fermented).

- **Try eating fermented foods** – sauerkraut and kefir. As a dairy product, kefir is fermented and doesn't normally cause problems. Some cheeses are thought to help with the kinds of bacteria that are naturally found in them – like Roquefort cheese.

- **Try supplementing with probiotic capsule**s – Culturelle is a good one, or get a recommendation from a professional.

- **If you suffer from bloating** – a broad spectrum digestive enzymes might help or digestive bitters.

- **Sometimes specific diets help specific conditions** – like IBS, but you still need help to identify what the root cause is. Taking away trigger foods will manage the symptoms in the short term.

- **Deal with stress** –it shuts down the digestive juices, among many other effects.

- **If constipated** – obviously check if you are drinking enough fluid; water is essential, or taking some powdered magnesium (as magnesium ascorbate) might loosen things up. But the foundation of a good diet is key.

- **Eat plenty of fruits and vegetables** – make sure your diet is full of fruits and vegetables, which contain the kind of fibre that friendly bacteria like to make their homes in.

LOOK AFTER YOUR LIVER

Your liver is responsible for processing hormones and breaking down toxins. The liver has a lot of work to do and by and large we tend to ignore our poor livers. Although the liver is capable of regeneration, actual scarring on the liver (permanent damage) is sometimes only picked up when liver function is at a fraction of capacity.

- **Over-drinking alcohol regularly** – more than a couple of glasses a week is not good for this marginalized organ. Alcohol is not good for the brain – it is a neurotoxin (brain toxin). Some people's genetics are not so well adapted to drinking any quantity of alcohol (these genetic deviations are called *snips*). The amount people can tolerate varies quite a bit.

- **Digestive bitters help the liver** – typically digestive bitters contain dandelion and milk thistle, which helps the liver's detoxification pathways. NAC (N-acetylcysteine), which comes as a supplement, can help the detoxification pathways function better, but of course that isn't a free pass to go mad and drink the bar dry.

- **Looking after your digestion** – this will help your liver because elimination will be better and the liver won't have to work so hard.

- **Looking after your hormonal health** - will also help your liver, as it has to cope with hormones. There are other tricks to looking after your hormones, for example managing stress and blood sugar will also help manage hormones.

- **Minimize your exposure to chemicals in the home** - cleaning products, perfumes and even makeup, which is absorbed through your skin. Chipping away at improvement over time is the key.

- **Green juices, and smoothies** - can help give your liver the raw materials to help it do its job (it needs certain vitamins and minerals; obviously vegetables are full of minerals in plentiful supply).

LOOK AFTER YOUR BRAIN

We've learned that your body and brain are connected. But, the big worry these days is the number of people who develop dementia-like problems in old age. Professor Dale Bredesen from University of California, Los Angeles and The Buck institute of Ageing is shining a light on the dark corners of dementia and Alzheimer's. He thinks that diet plays a huge part in avoiding these conditions. Good diet, rich in the micronutrients that protect brain function, might be key, although there are other factors. But diet by far is the biggest player.

- **Looking after your gut health will help your mental health outcomes** – those little bacteria are communicating with our brains.

- **Make sure that you have enough essential fats** – especially those Omega 3 fats (or supplement with Krill oil).

- **Look after the powerhouses in your cells (the mitochondria)** – they are powered by micronutrients, especially CoQ10, all the B vitamins, magnesium and antioxidant nutrients found widely in the diet.

- **Make sure your diet is varied** – good quality, and organic if possible. Food grown in poor soil is likely to be more depleted in nutrients; hence, why organic is important.

- **Another worry might be exposure to electro-magnetic frequencies (EMFs)** – primarily through the use of smart phones and wi-fi. Some scientists believe that EMF interferes with how mitochondria function. Our brains are stuffed full of mitochondria that need looking after. Until they agree that we are actually frying our brains, we can use the speaker function, special headphones, normally called "Blue-Tube" head phones (they have a portion of the wire as an air tube) so that the radiation doesn't go straight to the brain, so the theory goes. Switch the wi-fi off at night, when the brain is in repair function.

- **Make sure that inflammation in your body is reduced as much as possible** - by eating plenty of fresh foods, fruits and vegetables. Avoid too much inflammatory foods such as meat and grain in the diet. They produce chemicals that produce inflammation - heat or fire in the body - which is what the word means, as you Latin scholars will attest.

- **There is a correlation that sugar might play a part in the development of dementia** - in part because it overloads the mitochondria, causing them to function poorly. But, more studies need to be conducted before it is widely accepted that sugar is really the big bad wolf. My view is, why wait? You only need to look at societies that don't have sugar and associated disease outcomes. Be a leader, not a follower - remember to use your instincts and common sense above all else.

We use nutritional resources to counterbalance the effects of stress.

REDUCE YOUR STRESS LEVELS

We were designed to have very focused moments of highly stressful events, like getting eaten by that famous sabre-toothed tiger. We weren't designed for prolonged (chronic) stress, like wondering if we will have enough money next month for the mortgage. Many experts believe that this is a huge player in our health outcomes. We use nutritional resources – blood sugar management, micro and macro nutrients – to counterbalance the effects of stress. If you have poor resources, then coping with on-going stress or bursts of stress will be more difficult.

Stress affects the body in many ways:

- Affects your hormones by stealing other hormones, like progesterone, to make cortisol, and disturbing balance in the body, eating up those resources.

- Disturbs the microbiome – your little bacteria city.

- Steals nutrients like magnesium (magnesium is a key mineral for your mitochondrial health) and many other nutrients like zinc, B vitamins, vitamin C and many others.

- Changes the relationship of carbon dioxide to oxygen in the body, which imbalances your biochemical systems.

STRESS NUBETTE

- Be realistic about what you can change and what you have to accept.

- Try mindfulness - a type of mind training, originally inspired by the Buddhist principles of meditation. It uses the focused attention of your mind to stay in the present. If you like using apps - Headspace is brilliant for understanding and using mindfulness.

- Go for a walk - yes, and breathe. This connects the two parts of the nervous system:. the alarm part and the recovery part.

- Go to the chiropractor to look into the neuro aspects of spine health (i.e., they are holistic). Apparently, your circuits can almost get stuck on a loop, causing anxiety. Even if you don't have a problem, visit a chiropractor for a semi-regular reboot of your muscular skeletal system.

- Don't listen to the news - really, the endless analysis is just someone else's mad thinking.

- Eating to balance blood sugar will help straighten out cortisol to some extent. Avoid food that is sweet, fluffy (with a light density) and white (processed) and aim for food that has low density (needs chewing) and is fibrous, including proteins and good fats (see the section on fats).

- Don't have too much caffeine, if at all. Whatever they are telling you about the epigallocatechins in green tea or antioxidants in coffee, the caffeine will make you jumpy.

- Some vitamins help stress – B vitamins (for the nervous system), especially B5 (but take in a B complex), vitamin C, magnesium and some herbs like Siberian Ginseng and Ashwagandha.

- Keep a sense of humour and perspective.

- If you are eating real food but are stressed, you will need to eat salt in your diet – use Himalayan pink salt. Salt, despite all the bad publicity, is a vital nutrient. It's all about what works for you. Some people who avoid salt can get symptoms such as a racing heart. The nub of this is eating enough potassium (which is abundant in fruits and vegetables).

EXERCISE NUBETTE

Exercise helps transport nutrients to the cells, and building muscle helps your metabolic rate. Exercise builds bone, reduces stress and has all sorts of other benefits. It turns out that hyper-exercising in the evenings at the gym isn't the thing. Movement is. So, move more, constantly.

- Sitting (for long periods) is the new smoking, meaning that it is just as detrimental to your health - consider a standing desk.
- Yoga, Pilates - you can get an app that takes you through simple regimes if you don't have a local class. Personally, I do a mixture of both.
- Walking in nature - even at the local park. No technology required.
- Taking a break and walking on your lunch break. Breathe.
- Time - what are you saying no to when you say yes to sitting at your desk at all hours, hunching your shoulders? Cramping your stomach, giving rise to digestive issues that's what.

BASE CAMP

Just do a couple of things to move you on to a little personal improvement. Remember, you really don't have to be perfect.

1. Get up from your chair at least every 20 minutes – go and get a herbal tea or a drink of water. Setting a notification on your phone can be useful, just to remind you.

2. Keep your phone in airplane mode as much as possible, especially if you are carrying it on your body (holding it or it's in your pocket).

3. If you work in an office, make sure you take a lunch break, even if it's 20 minutes to actually eat your lunch, not eating your lunch while multi-tasking.

CAMP 1

If you have ticked off everything in Base Camp, then go for the upgrade.

1. Get a mindfulness app and give yourself optimum recovery time. Mindfulness reboots the brain. It turns out the brain is quite 'plastic', meaning flexible. New neural pathways are formed even in old age, but we have to give our brain a period of 'off' and not always be 'on', which we are in the modern world.

2. Switch off your wi-fi router at night - or get a wired Faraday Cage to put the router in at night.

3. Here's a weird one. Go for a walk in the park or in nature, and where possible (and if safe) go barefoot. We are electrical beings and being in touch with the earth literally grounds us. Or get a pair of leather-soled shoes; it turns out all this rubber (on our shoes), isn't optimal for our health (who knew?).

We are electrical beings and being in touch with the earth literally grounds us.

SUMMIT

Wow – I am impressed! You ROCK. Obviously you've ticked off everything at Base Camp and Camp 1.

1. Consider a piece of tech that measures your brain waves, so you can learn to improve your meditation. It gives you feedback in real time. The only one I know is called Muse. Apparently, the frequencies emitted are extremely low, but use the blue air tube headphones. As an aside, never use Bluetooth earpieces until the research is well and truly in. Emerging evidence suggests that cell phones might affect the blood-brain barrier's disintegration. This fragile barrier is all there is between your brain being somewhat protected from outside sources and not.

2. Why not invest in a standing desk? These days, a lot of companies are open to this idea. They don't want you to be sick. If you work from home, you can adapt your desk easily with a little digging on the internet to find out how. Going hell for leather at the gym at 6.00pm does not have the benefits of continual movement and actually using the body you have.

3. Don't wait until you get sick – why not consider investing in a full body health check. Find a practitioner who uses functional medicine and get some baseline tests. The test names will vary from lab to lab, but generally

you need to look at your minerals, heavy metals exposure, vitamin D levels and inflammatory markers. This gives you a baseline and can give you clues years before any of these markers could contribute to disease.

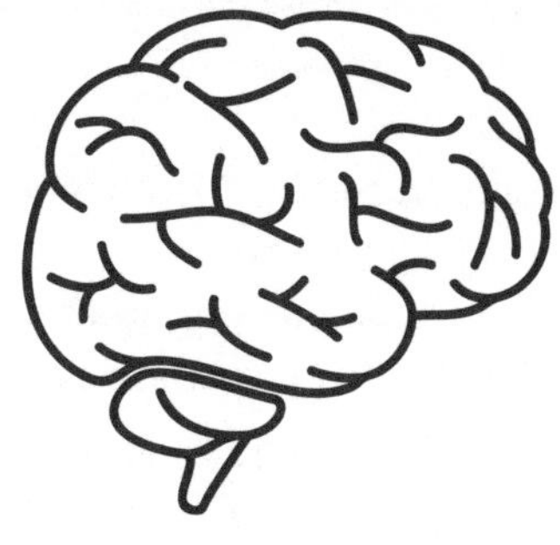

STRATEGY 4: LOOK AFTER THE LITTLE THINGS IN LIFE

We've been introduced to the microbiome – the friendly guys in our gut (and we have some strategies to look after those guys) – and we have met our other little friends, the mitochondria. The mitochondria are little organelles in our cells that produce our energy, by way of a reminder. It was originally thought that they were bacteria and had become integrated into our system. It was probably mitochondria that took us from breathing anaerobically (without oxygen) to aerobic breathing (with oxygen).

Some research scientists think that these little guys are key to understanding critical diseases like cancer. Professor Thomas Seyfried of Boston College thinks that it is poor mitochondria health that make the cells produce faulty genetic copies in diseases like cancer, rather than the other way around (i.e., it's not faulty genetics, but when these little powerhouses go wrong, they can lead to poor outcomes). But as you can imagine, that view is controversial, as there is so much investment in other theories.

If these little guys produce our energy, shouldn't we just look after them until everyone can agree on that one?

LOOKING AFTER YOUR MITOCHONDRIA

- Make sure that you are not over-exposing yourself to electromagnetic fields.

- Your biggest control over your innate biochemistry, including your mitochondria, is through your diet.

- Specifically, these nutrients will help mitochondria health - CoQ10, magnesium, B vitamins and antioxidants (a range of nutrients that mop up damage), the nutrients that drive the Krebs Cycle (a bit of biochemical fancy footwork that turns the wheel of producing energy in your cells). But, don't eat foods high in CoQ10; that is just faddy. Eat organic meats, sardines, and vegetables like cauliflower. In general, you should try to improve the quality and variety of food in your diet.

- To counteract the effects of modern life, you might need to supplement. But don't just eat masses of oranges because they are high in vitamin C; that is madness and will make you deficient in other things, and will drive you crazy trying to figure out what.

- Specifically, the mitochondria don't like sugar. A study at Yale University found that sugar changed the shape and function of the mitochondria.

UPGRADE

Fasting can help your little mitochondria energy factories – even just lengthening the time you are without food overnight. Eat your evening meal earlier, and then eat breakfast later. You are, in effect, eating your meals within a window of say seven or eight hours (e.g., between 11.00am and 6.00pm). This helps the mitochondria function better, as they are not always trying to process food. Doing this just a couple of times a week will be beneficial. Skipping dinner occasionally will also help give the guys a little rest. Only do this if your blood sugar is already stable, or you will find that you are just shaky and bad tempered.

Look at saunas and plunge pools as a way of stimulating your mitochondria – those Scandinavians know a thing or two about that! The idea of challenging your little guys probably simulates our ancient biochemistry – when we would have experienced challenges to our bodily systems, e.g., extreme heat, cold or our food supply drying up. Then we would have had a bounce-back – bad times followed by good times.

A WORD ON VITAMIN D

Vitamin D really acts like a hormone, rather than a vitamin. Almost 87% of people in the UK are deficient, according to some estimates. Vitamin D is important for all kinds of processes in the body and especially associated with healthy, strong immunity. We make vitamin D through sun exposure on the skin, although there are some dietary sources of vitamin D (include oily fish, beef liver, egg yolks, cheese and some varieties of mushroom).

Get your vitamin D tested at the end of the summer – this will give you what should be your optimum. If you are low at this point, you really will need to correct the level.

Get your level tested in March – this is your low point of the year (in the Northern Hemisphere or other way around for the Southern Hemisphere).

It's best still to get some safe sun exposure. But burning is sun damage, so that is not what you are aiming for.

I find the spray vitamin D (liquid doses of vitamin D delivered in a spray format) very good for ease of remembering to take. Again, there is a massive disagreement among the professionals about how much to take. I typically take around 3,000 IU in the winter (but remember, I know this is how much I need to take according to the test). Vitamin D in mega doses could be toxic, so don't go mad without knowing your level. A modest 500 to 1,000 IU should not cause a problem. But remember, you are unique, and one man's drink is another man's poison.

Vitamin D in mega doses could be toxic, so don't go mad without knowing your level.

BASE CAMP

Start here for little hacks to take you to the next level:

1. Get your vitamin D tested and definitely supplement if you need to. Vitamin D works with vitamin K2, so supplement with that, too. I find the good quality spray versions of this wonderful for actually remembering to take these two work horses.

2. Getting enough sleep is really important. Amounts vary, but usually between seven and eight hours. There are a few people genetically who can get by on less, but honestly, they are a rarity. While we are asleep, the cellular cleaning team comes in and clears the old debris in our cells. This helps the mitochondria do a better job and keeps them in tip-top shape.

3. Move more. You have a circulatory system (heart, arteries, veins), but the waste products in your lymph system rely on movement to function optimally. Your lymph system is like a drain, which takes away the waste products in the body.

CAMP 1

1. Really get into looking after your mitochondria. That means always eat organic. Think about nutrients that those little guys thrive on; ubiquinol is a good one to start with (it is the precursor to its better-known end product, CoQ10). Consider supplementing with magnesium. Very new research (by biochemist Dr Martin Pall) suggests that EMFs fiddle around with how calcium is handled in your cells, and that magnesium might help mitigate this somewhat. This, of course, is very controversial, and the use of magnesium to right this balance is only theoretical currently. Again, you are in the driver's seat of your health, so do your research and find out what you think is true.

2. Give those little mitochondrial dudes a shock. Try switching the shower to cold for just a few seconds or as long as you can stand. Three times a week is probably enough.

3. Intermittent fasting is choosing a time window within which to eat. You might try to push out how long you go without eating after you wake up (so eat breakfast later), and eat dinner earlier. This gives the body and digestion a rest, and those little mitochondria can get on and do their job better. There are a huge number of animal studies that look at calorie restriction to prolong life – but is that really practical? Intermittent fasting might be worth looking into as it's easier to apply. You must make sure your blood sugar is stable before taking any of these upgrades, or you will just feel starving and dive into the biscuit tin.

SUMMIT

If you loved Base Camp and Camp 1 – try this!

1. Consider a fast. There are hundreds of way to look into this further. Once you get the hang of intermittent fasting, then taking it a step further and a five day fast will be a doddle. Obviously, there are lots of different ways to do a fast, from a juice fast to a water fast. The method really depends on where you are on your journey (even at the Summit). Check out Dr Jason Fung's Book, *The Complete Guide to Fasting*. You'll need to research this further to fast safely, so get informed. Fasting gives the body a chance to get rid of cells that are past their sell-by date, so it's essentially a bodily spring clean. Fasting also rests the digestive system and the liver.

   Bonus: Fasting is cheap! No food to buy for a few days!

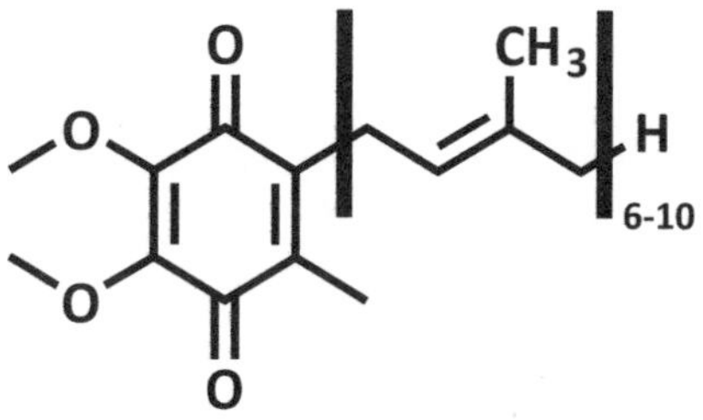

STRATEGY 5:
FOCUS ON QUALITY

We have laboured the concept of real food and I hope by now you understand what that means. Real food has not been processed, and it is fresh, it is whole food, i.e., food that hasn't been manufactured into anything else. By and large it is not commoditized – meaning that it can be stored forever and made into something with an added value too (e.g., putting it into a packet). Also, buy food from sources other than the supermarket if at all possible and practical. Remember, this might be an upgrade – so start by just buying fresh food from wherever possible.

WHY FOCUS ON QUALITY

Food, particularly organic fresh food (and not organic twaddle that has been turned into a product through marketing), is more likely to have good micronutrients (the vitamins and minerals your body needs).

Organic food is more likely to not have been grown with pesticides, and therefore the residues will not be on your food. We don't really know the collective effect of different pesticides on our foods. The food industry says that these are in microscopic amounts, but the effects of the cocktail of these substances have not been adequately tested (long term) on human health. If you don't believe that organic is good for you, then look at how organic and biodynamic agriculture could be good for the planet. We know that a class of pesticide is killing the bees (*neonicotinoids*) – so if you don't care about you and your family, at least try to care what we are doing to our planet.

Realizing that our current system is unsustainable, by helping even in a small way to value food and the thought and effort that goes into it, we could start a food revolution. Food democracy isn't just about looking after ourselves, but ensuring that we all get good quality food. Idealism, certainly, but we have to correct the balance of how we eat. Many of us are suffering from the direct consequence of the world of food going so far towards industrialized, dead food, and it's killing us. We are literally killing ourselves with our own knives and forks.

BASE CAMP

1. Buy organic if you can or at least try to buy fresh food. Look at your budget and how you might afford it – do you need that Sky subscription? That is one week's food.

2. Carve out time to prepare your food. It is more time consuming, so get your family to help. You don't have to produce some Nigella, finger-licking, sumptuous dish every night. Leftovers are fine.

CAMP 1

1. Consider taking a cooking course if you really haven't got the basics.

2. Put boundaries in place around work (i.e., get home at a reasonable time). Plan ahead or you will be home early with no food.

3. Buy local. Look into groups like the Food Assembly (referred to earlier), which assemble local food (even in a city) and you pick it up. This is becoming more popular and widespread. Buying your food from someone you could potentially have a conversation with is the aim, rather than mindlessly picking up more stuff in plastic and throwing it in the bin at the end of the week.

SUMMIT

1. Do you have space to grow your own food? If you have a small outside space, raised boxed beds are an idea. If your have a larger space, how much can you give over to growing your own delicious vegetables? The big consideration here is time. It really provides two benefits in one: gardening is meditation in action, and you'll soak up all that lovely vitamin D by being outside.

STRATEGY 6: FAT IS OUR FRIEND

Learning to love fat is so counterintuitive that our minds struggle to make sense of it. Isn't fat the devil incarnate? We have been so influenced by the theory that calorie counting is the only game in town with nutrition. We have seen the adverts on the television that show a picture of a blocked drain, threatening us with what happens to saturated fat in the body (it blocks the arteries in that model). What kind of idiots do they take us for? They suggest the body is a kind of machine that food is poured into from the top, like a funnel (the mouth) and it gets stuck in our tubes (or circulatory systems). Essentially they are treating us like fools. The digestive system, enzymes, our long digestive tracts, and the liver all play a part in how fat is handled in the body. We are not traction engines.

The point is that the thinking has flip-flopped back in favour of fat. The movement to replace fat resulted in more carbohydrate consumption. That changed eating habits and an increase in soft drink consumption, snacking, treat foods and more consumerism around food. It changed our eating habits forever. Additionally, there is a really dodgy kind of fat in carbohydrate baked goods – trans fats. This is not a type of fat our body likes, and it's been taken off the generally recognized safe lists, and manufacturers are replacing this fat. But with what, we ask?

BENEFICIAL FATS

It turns out, we can utilize all sorts of energy sources through food, and we can burn fat in favour of carbohydrates. When we burn carbohydrates, they burn 'dirty'. They leave a biochemical trail that has to be mopped up by our hardworking body systems, especially the processed form of carbohydrates. We are not talking about vegetables, which give all sorts of other benefits, including nutrients and fibre. When we burn the right kind of fat, its metabolic imprint is not so onerous. Lowering your sweet, fluffy and white dietary component is important, though, for all the reasons discussed. Remember, carbohydrates are not evil if they are from real sources, rather than always relying on processed forms. Fresh is best! Any vegetable is a carbohydrate – eat a moderate amount of whole grains if you want to and, as an upgrade, make them the gluten free grains.

What we need to understand is that there are some kinds of fat that are essential. Hang on to your hats, guys. These fats are labelled 'essential fats', which means they can't be made by your own body; you need to eat these to add them to your system. Fats run our hormonal systems and our brains. Hormones affect how your body works metabolically – how it processes food and how all the body's systems work.

There are two essential types of fats: Omega 3 (mostly from fish, with a few other sources); and Omega 6 (mostly from nuts, grains and a few other sources). In a Western diet, the ratio is way out of whack – we should make sure we have more Omega 3 in our diet. By the way, sometimes you see Omega 9 listed in supplements – it's a nifty bit of marketing, because Omega 9 isn't actually essential.

FATS TO AIM FOR

- Avocados – they are monounsaturated fat, by the way. That is a type of fat that is good, but not essential.
- Nuts – they tend to be full of Omega 6 fat, but walnuts are a source of Omega 3.
- Oily fish – go for the smaller types of fish like herring, sardines, sprats and mackerel. Our polluted planet is making the bigger fish way too toxic for our consumption. These provide Omega 3 and are essential for good health.
- Butter and lard, organic goose or organic duck (lard is very stable for cooking) – this type of

fat is saturated; not essential, but useful to keep us full.

- Coconut oil/fat – it's actually a saturated fat. Saturated fats are very stable, chemically speaking, so when you cook with it, it doesn't damage in the heat, like polyunsaturated fat (sunflower oil and vegetable oil).

In general, if any company has a budget to advertise to you about their products' benefits, don't believe them. They want your money and couldn't give a care about the long-term health effects. Don't fall for it.

NUTRITION NUBETTE

- Fat has got a bad rap and for more than 40 years has been demonized.
- Beneficial types of fat keep you full and feeling satisfied and stop you from diving into the cookie jar.
- Beneficial fat comes from real food – yes, yes!
- You may be so caught up in the calorie-counting theory that this will seem to be a bit mad. Beyond your immediate ancestors (i.e., great-great grandmother), think aquatic apes, searching out fatty treats to build that great big brain.

Think about
the seasons.

BASE CAMP

1. Swap out poor-quality carbohydrate for ones that give something back – like nutrients! Lovely organic vegetables and some whole grains if you like. Don't eat a high-twaddle and high-fat diet!

2. Make sure you have some MASH fish three times a week. MASH fish are Mackerel, Anchovies, Sardines and Herring. These smaller fish are lower in the toxins that we have polluted our own seas and oceans with, with scant regard for the fish or our own health.

3. If you are vegetarian, see how you get on with Flaxseed oil as an essential fat. It doesn't suit everyone; some people don't process it well, as they lack the enzymes to do the job. See how it suits you.

CAMP 1

1. Play around with the ratios of fat in your diet and see how you feel. The new Keto-type diets are very high in fat, low in carbohydrates and moderate in protein. However, it is probably more sensible to cycle in and out of phases so that you are not doing this all the time.

2. Think about the seasons. Our ancient relatives feasted in the autumn (on ripe fruit), ate more fat in the winter and celebrated with plenty in the summer. I'm not sure what they did in the spring, probably sighed a huge sigh that winter was over. Variation is always the key.

SUMMIT

1. Stop buying plastic water bottles because, as we know, that and other plastic ends up in the sea and kills both the fish and you (eventually).

2. Filter your water with a jug. The one I use filters the water and is slightly alkaline (Biocera).

3. Buy fish that is sustainable only, no exceptions.

STRATEGY 7: FOOD FAD OR FOOD REALITY?

The thing about nutritional science is that just as we get used to one theory, another one comes along and blows everything out of the water. That is why I think we should be as flexible as possible in terms of how we view food (and nutrition). So, with the fads that come and go, which ones should we believe and which ones are just fads?

FAD-A-BILITY POINT SCALE
0 = IT'S A MAD FAD
10 = THERE IS PROBABLY SOME TRUTH IN IT

HIGH PROTEIN, LOW CARBS DIETS

This type of high-protein diet was made famous by Dr Atkins (apparently, *The Atkins Diet* at one point outsold the Bible). What does your instinct tell you about this? Even without my nutritional training, it tells me that getting protein at any cost is mad. Getting your protein fix from sausages (what is in the sausage) or from bacon, cured in all sorts of noxious chemicals (nitrates) is bonkers. This type of diet was not new, even at the time. The Banting Diet (1860-ish) was based on the same model. What happened? With both of these high-protein diets, people lost weight. The problem comes with the amount of protein; excessive protein may stimulate *mTOR*, which promotes growth in the body, and unchecked and rapid growth is not a good thing for cells. In addition, very low carbohydrate diets long term may cause the thyroid gland to malfunction ultimately. These diets tend to be very low in fibre which causes constipation. Reducing or eliminating twaddle carbohydrate will be a good thing (for example pasta, bread, loads of rice), but carbohydrate is not evil per se (for example sweet potatoes, vegetables). As with everything there is a Goldilocks point of ideal balance between carbohydrate and protein – just the right amount and the right quality.

FAD-A-BILITY POINTS = 4

By reducing carbs, you will lose weight but increasing protein by any means, living on sausages, is potty.

HIGH-FIBRE DIETS

High-fibre diets were made famous by the F-Plan Diet (now the Amish Diet). A big problem with processed food is that the fibre is removed, because fibre doesn't freeze or process that well. So, having a fibrous diet is great. The trouble with the F-Plan was the amount of commodity carbohydrate they added back (i.e., rice, pasta and other grains).

FAD-A-BILITY POINTS = 5

- Adding fibre is good, but make sure it is from fresh food. By just eating a better, fresher diet you'll get all the fibre you need without focussing on it.

DAVE ASPREY AND BULLET-PROOF COFFEE

The main point of this diet is upping the fat with moderate protein intake and low carbs. Despite the faddy coffee vibe – you add grass fed butter and coconut oil (or MCT oil, a type of coconut oil to coffee in the morning instead of breakfast), I think the basic premise is sound. This regime works by keeping you in a fasting state from when you had your last meal to when you have your first eaten meal (i.e. not the coffee but when you eat). Added to that this regime has low carbs (i.e. eliminating sweet, fluffy and white carbs, moderate protein is good, because you don't want to be in growth unless you are a body builder and even then, excessive amounts of protein is mad in my opinion). The main drive is concentrating on adding high beneficial fats to the diet. The trick is to cycle the regime so that you are not producing ketones (a byproduct of not eating carbohydrates) all the time or you could crash and burn.

FAD-A-BILITY POINTS = 7.5

Good fats, moderate protein and no sweets, white and fluffy. Bit faddy on the coffee vibe – but surprisingly effective. By the way, although people do lose weight on this regime, it is for the cognitive benefits that people claim is the major player here. Remember fat and the brain?

NO WHEAT AND DAIRY DIETS

Due to the way wheat is grown and then put into baked processed products, I personally don't think this is faddy. Wheat affects the tight junctions in the gut, giving some people digestive issues, for starters. I avoid wheat, but sometimes I might just have one or two slices of delicious homemade bread (the lower the gluten the better, so I might go for spelt).

Dairy, again, is by and large industrially farmed. Go for yogurt (which has the benefit of the bacteria) or butter, which actually has butyric acid that helps the lining of the gut.

FAD-A-BILITY POINTS = 7.5

I am in favour of this diet. I have seen too many patients who worked to eliminate these foods (being careful to replace with other choices – spelt or rye, with great benefit to digestion and well-being). But remember, you have to do the rest, like eating more vegetables!

Vegetarians avoid meat and fish, but generally will eat eggs, and cheese. **Vegans** don't eat any product that comes from an animal or the labour of an animal, like honey from bees.

These are fine, but watch your blood sugar and eat real food. Watch for deficiencies in terms of nutrients: commonly iron in menstruating women, and generally vitamin B 12 and zinc). It's easy just to increase your intake of poor-quality carbohydrates, resorting to white and fluffy, so be careful.

We should be
as flexible as
possible
in terms of
how we
view food.

5:2 DIETS

The principal of 5:2 diets is that you eat quite normally for five days and then do a semi-fast on the other two days by cutting down on calories. This diet was made famous by Dr Michael Mosley.

This diet has all sorts of studied benefits – not least, it gives your cells an extension on their life. Cells are programmed to die once they get to the end of their genetic code, and this regimen seems to stretch out this process.

The problem is when people do this as a temporary fix. Fasting, without a balanced blood sugar, will have you diving into the cookie jar, and makes women (in particular, but men too) obsessed with food. It's actually easier to just skip dinner sometimes. Extending when you eat breakfast to later in the day and having dinner earlier means you are eating in an 8 to 10-hour window and leaving more time overnight without piling in more grub. This is intermittent fasting.

FAD-A-BILITY POINTS = 4

This gets a low score because of the manner of the fasting method, which potentially has a bingeing rebound, not because it doesn't have huge scientific merit, which it does. Watch yourself if you have any issues around food psychologically.

SUMMARY

All diets or regimens probably have a little truth behind them.

BASE CAMP

1. Balance the blood sugar.

2. Eat real food – unprocessed – and good fats.

3. Your protein intake should be reasonable, but not excessive.

CAMP 1

1. Eliminate the sweet, white and fluffy carbohydrates (twaddle by our definition here, because these groups of food are void of nutrients).

SUMMIT

1. Consider intermittent fasting (describe above), which works on all sorts of biochemical outcomes (resting digestion, those cell extensions and your mitochondrial health). The mitochondria do better with a bit of a break and, in fact, there are some experts who are saying that all degenerative disease might be an overload of the mitochondria.

STRATEGY 8: RECONNECTING WITH YOUR BODY

We are all living at a mad pace. We don't pay attention unless something goes terribly wrong with the vehicle that we inhabit – this shell we call our body. It's when our bodily health starts limiting our choices that we start to do all the things we should have done all along. It's a unique and human quality that we live for today and don't really think about the future of our health and our food. We'll grab something and pay the health debt tomorrow. We were biochemically programmed to live our lives like a beautiful firefly, a brief appearance on the stage of life, and then BOOM – infectious disease, war, childbirth. We weren't programmed for a long life into old age (although some ancient people did make it to old age if they avoided those pitfalls).

The point is that most degenerative disease will be brought on by our choices. Because humans are so adaptable and resilient, it takes a lot to kill us. Eventually, it stores up as bad surprises and bites us hard on the bum. Metabolic disease is when the body systems seize up and our hormones start misfiring, and the feedback mechanisms fail to kick in.

Mitochondrial overload is the overloading of our energy powerhouses with too much, for too long, and this will take a toll. Take note of what your body is telling you and look after it. Remember, too, what your emotions are telling you and don't ignore the signals that act as a rudder in your life. Your emotions will store in your muscles and body, and they can suddenly pop out at all sorts of inconvenient times.

HEAD PEOPLE
– THOSE WHO DON'T THINK ABOUT THEIR BODY OR THE ENVIRONMENT

- Ignore little health niggles (these are your body putting you in an amber light).
- Could never imagine living without their phone for a minute.
- Think that work is life.
- Don't exercise – no time. You don't have to exercise formally, but you do have to move.
- Think that having a laugh is a bit frivolous and has no purpose. Actually, laughter produces all sorts of positive hormone cascades.
- Think that dealing with stress is for wimps.
- Fill all the little gaps of life with activities.

- Would rather watch terrible TV programmes (reality shows) than have a life of their own.
- Don't care what happens to food waste or discarded plastic (who needs whales and dolphins anyway?) .
- Don't care how our food is grown, as long as they can get to the supermarket (and do the shopping with headphones on, in case someone tries to speak to them).
- Purely driven by food price, rather than quality.
- Want the latest thing all the time and think that shopping is a legitimate hobby.

+ CONSCIOUS PEOPLE – THOSE WHO KNOW THEY HAVE A BODY

- Know that health is a long-term game, and short-term blips don't matter that much. It all goes horribly wrong from time to time.

- Realize that technology is a wonderful tool, but for now they are in charge.

- Are respectful of their bodies, but not obsessed.

- Cook their food from scratch.

- Care about themselves and others with regard to food waste and pollution.

- Know that work is not life and have that in proportion to contributing to community, family or someone else but themselves (at least some of the time).

- Know that their food choices will make a huge difference to how we can influence farming, agriculture and our futures.

NUTRITION NUBETTE

- Really pay attention to the clues your poor old body is trying to give you. If you are tired, are you getting enough sleep? Is it what you are eating? Is it something more serious (e.g., your thyroid or something else)?

- If you have hormonal problems or digestive problems or any minor health problem – what can you do about it?

- Invest now. Some degenerative diseases have a really long lead time – like dementia. You can at least have a bash at avoiding what might seem like an inevitability.

STRATEGY 9: RECONNECT WITH YOUR FOOD AND LAND

The number of overweight people is increasing worldwide. This has happened fairly recently, and we are seeing a global crisis with diabetes (a diet-related disease) and obesity as a result. This was caused by changes in farming policy of the US. More globalization makes it easier to distribute cheap food products, nutrient-void carbohydrates, in such abundance and at such an attractive price point that you believe you'd be mad to prepare your own food, especially with the longer hours and all the family being forced to work to keep up with the costs of mortgages, TVs, the latest fridge freezer, and other time-saving white goods. While we remain so disconnected from our food and want quick fixes through acquiring more stuff, health issues that could be prevented by diet are set to rise.

My theory is that those of us interested in food will be the few remaining Homo Sapiens and eventually be made extinct – a bit like the sweet Neanderthals. We will be overtaken by tech man, who will have phones strapped on to their heads and be addicted to twaddle food. We will have polluted and killed off our planet, and luckily, we will have figured out how to fill the atmosphere around Mars with space junk, old wrappers, and noxious chemicals, and we can colonize that, as Professor Stephen Hawkins recently suggested.

Food connects us to our land, and the few people left growing food on it. It connects us to the reasons it matters that we invest money wisely, so that the custodians who will look after our future can work to save our planet. I know this sounds a bit doom and gloom, but as we go on to encroach on the land as urbanites and remain disconnected to the cost of poor agricultural choices, we honestly don't stand a chance as Homo Sapiens. Agriculture is the biggest polluter on the planet. We can't seriously ignore the fact that we are killing the birds and bees off with our arrogant disregard for other species. That is just the tip of the old melting iceberg. Glyphosates and other classes of chemicals are toxic to us, the animals, the sea, everything.

It might seem like we are doomed. But you can play a small part in changing this rather gloomy trajectory. Look at the change in cigarette smoking – how everyone smoked and now almost no one does. Yes, the government did have to legislate, but we can do it!

It might seem like we are doomed. But you can play a small part in changing this rather gloomy trajectory.

BASE CAMP

1. Buy the knobbly fruit and vegetables in your supermarket.

2. Watch a video of an intensely farmed operation. Then go and visit an organic farm - and try and live with yourself if you ignore the difference.

3. Don't believe the PR campaign that would have you believing that pesticides are the only option for our future. This is tech-man thinking that we have to manipulate everything. At least do your research and then make up your own mind. Don't just be one of the sheep that accepts the way things are heading.

CAMP 1

1. Buy organic food. Organic is kinder to the environment and might benefit you too. Beware of so-called food (of the twaddle variety) that has just been created into a product and has conned you. I know you are much too bright to fall for that one.

2. Buy seasonally where you live. Strawberries are only available in early summer in the UK. Really. Otherwise they are imported. Imported fruits and vegetables out of season have a footprint of miles, ultimately not good for our planet; nutrients degrade in transport. We have become very spoiled expecting out-of-season food (strawberries are a June treat in England, for example). What about supporting your own local farmers, what effect would this have for us and our health? Further, there is a school of nutritional thought that eating according to the seasons is something we have biochemically evolved to do. Eating more carbohydrates in times of plenty (fresh autumnal fruit), feasting in the winter for the relative lean period until March, rounding off with summer's abundance of fresh green produce, and relying less on cooked food (of course, this is Northern Hemisphere).

3. Support your local farm, ideally organic. That doesn't mean some fancy 'farm shop' where the food costs a million quid. There are a lot of great resources online if you can't find anything local. At least make it local to your country.

4. Get an organic box. If you can plan ahead, this can be cheaper than buying in a supermarket, a third of which you end up chucking out at the end of the week.

SUMMIT

1. Look into biodynamic agriculture and regenerative agriculture and get informed. Biodynamic agriculture looks at agriculture in terms of how it waves in with nature and the environment. Regenerative agriculture concentrates on the health of the top soil and how correct animal husbandry fits in with the improvement in the top soil.

STRATEGY 10: RECONNECT WITH FAMILY AND YOUR COMMUNITY

We've said that food connects us as humans – every celebration that involves the humble human focuses around food. Whether it is for the Queen's Jubilee Tea Parties, Christmas, Passover or breaking the Ramadan fast and everything in between. Eating alone? There isn't anything in our long history that has this as a template for our evolution. Anthropologists might have something to say, but to me it would seem that if you were eating alone as a human, you had somehow been ostracized by your tribe, an almost certain death in early societies.

BASE CAMP

1. If you are eating on your own, eat at a table or at least no multitasking (on the phone) and never eating while watching the news. Although you know in your head that the news is happening in a far-off land (hopefully), your biochemistry is preparing you for fight or flight – that mechanism shuts down your digestive system. You will not get the best from your food this way.

CAMP 1

1. Why not throw a dinner party once a month? This forces you to try different recipes, and eating together is what life is all about.

2. Make it a rule that, by and large, all your meals as a family are eaten together. Community and communication are key.

SUMMIT

The issue with good quality food is that it's OK if you can afford it or don't live in a food desert. What can you do to help your community (if you have achieved all the above?) Recently a friend and I helped transform our local Harvest Festival. The general message of helping your community can't be a bad one, in my humble opinion. Pick an activity to help your community, which could be helping a less able person with their garden, or become a youth leader.

Susie Cooke (renowned journalist, community activist and my friend) and I couldn't believe that the food distributed to food banks was only twaddle food. Why should I eat good food, but the rest of the community and those who need it be palmed off with junk food? Isn't it something we should at least aspire to, that those who are most vulnerable in our communities have a right to proper food? Food plays a huge part in good mental health, as we have discussed. We focused on getting people to bring good, seasonal food to the Harvest Festival, with homemade bread as the communion (to share – i.e., breaking bread), then we got the community to make seasonal soup from the produce, which we all shared. We raised quite a few bob. Obviously, it would have been great to extend this pop-up soup kitchen to those who need it, so they could get a really great meal too, but the distribution is tricky. Can't we dream of how we can change this? All the biggest 'revolutions' in history have started with just an idea.

Next idea: to get my city (it is a small one) to share a meal together.

WHAT COULD YOU DO TO GET YOUR COMMUNITY MORE INTERESTED IN GREAT QUALITY FOOD OR FOOD DEMOCRACY?

- Shop local. This will give back something to your community.

- Organize a trip to a local organic farm.

- Volunteer to share a meal with an older person in the community. You don't have to do it every week, even if this is one of your own relations.

- For Sunday lunch, invite a group of friends and focus around food of the best quality you can afford.

- Remember your food choices affect your family, your community and soil health, and the ultimate health of the planet.

PART 6
YOUR STRATEGY: THE SHORT VERSION

As a reminder, those of you starting out on your nutritional journey, begin at Base camp. If you have sussed everything at Base Camp, then move to Camp 1, and then of course aim for the summit.

BASE CAMP

Buy real food (from a supermarket). This means food that hasn't been turned into anything else. Be aware of the packaging. Don't check the ingredients on the back of the pack – if you are, you are buying processed food.

Review your structures – boundaries and time. You may need to refocus; producing good food doesn't happen by magic:

1. Eat breakfast. Try real porridge made with water, real fruit and yogurt or boiled egg, rye soldiers, or nut butters on rye (almond, cashew). Eating breakfast balances the blood sugar and all sorts of other hormones. Never have twaddle cereal or muffins and don't eat at your desk.

2. Don't stress about getting dinner 'right' for now, just focus on breakfast – more change will come from there.

3. Invent your own breakfast, but you must try to have a bit of protein and good fat (see above for what that means), so you could have muesli with loads of nuts.

4. Plan your meals on a meal planner (and accept that it will go horribly wrong).

5. Move more, even if it means getting up from your desk more often.

6. Never eat your lunch or any other meal at your desk or wandering around the streets.

CAMP 1

1. Eat breakfast. Go for the savoury version: egg, avocado, good-quality smoked salmon, sheep cheese, mackerel, sardines, nut butters with rye or flaxseed crackers.

2. Don't eat sweet, fluffy and white food - carbohydrates are not evil, but don't go for the commercial commodity type unless in moderation (i.e., not loads of rice, pasta or mashed potatoes if at all). Eat sweet potatoes and vegetables as your carbohydrates. If you eliminate carbohydrates entirely, this strategy can crash the thyroid. Enjoy a little sweet potato, parsnip or other root vegetable at night in moderation.

3. Eat grass-fed meat (if you eat meat), which is higher in Omega 3 fat.

4. Eliminate wheat or choose spelt as a substitute. If you choose to eat wheat, or it doesn't seem to bother you, you should still note that commercial wheat products are twaddle.

5. Have organic dairy only, if you choose to eat it, and make sure that you eat it in moderation.

6. Manage stress, which impacts how your nutritional resources are used (i.e., all the goodness in your food is diverted to coping with the stress reaction). Set boundaries.

7. Move more. Get an app for yoga or Pilates. Consider a standing desk.

Always enjoy your food and keep that in the forefront of your mind.

SUMMIT

1. Make sure you have good structures to set boundaries at work, allocate prep time, cut down the tech time.

2. Push breakfast out a little later; this will give mitochondria a rest (only do this if your blood sugar is balanced).

3. You could try the coffee and butter, and MCT oil, but you don't have to be that detailed. Consider pushing the amount of time you go without eating. Eat within an eight-hour window. So, breakfast later, dinner earlier.

4. Eat real food that you have sourced locally, from an organic farm, box scheme, or the Food Assembly. Think about the impact your purchasing choices have on the world.

5. Eat together as a family, with a no-tech rule. That means no tech, whatever the apparent emergency. Do you want to become tech man or be part of the human race?

6. Invite someone in your community to lunch or just have a great Sunday lunch where you all gather.

7. Consider taking some basic supplements: I take a multi by Wild Nutrition, SeaGreens (for iodine), Krill oil (for Omega 3), magnesium at night (good for sleep and good for the mitochondria). If you have health issues, go and sort it out. Go to a nutritional therapist or other person who practices functional medicine; nutritional therapists should be BANT registered.

8. Always enjoy your food and keep that in the forefront of your mind. And most of all, don't forget the power you have to change our planet's future health by the choices you make with your food 'dollar'.

CONCLUSION

How the devil have we got to the point where more people in the world are overweight than starving? We're waddling around, sick, and waiting for the experts to dig us out of the mess of our own making. Taking away our instinct of what we know nurtures us leaves us confused and lacking confidence in *how* to eat to be our dynamic best. It's not our fault – we've been led a merry dance.

Our Western consumerism mind-set has fostered an idea that food is something we buy in the supermarket, and that food is just *product*, a commodity to be marketed to the masses. Food marketing treats us as if we are toddlers in a sweet shop – colourful packages, full of sugar and sometimes wholly addictive. The food industry cares nothing about our health; it's about profits. In short, it's about the bottom line of those who are peddling the marketing propaganda. The health claims printed on the pack – 'whole grain', 'part of your five a day', 'full of calcium and good for the bones': these messages are out of context and don't make sense on their own. They treat nutrition in a highly reductionist way, taking the nutrients out of the food and trying to make a health claim.

The only thing to do is to eat real, fresh food that doesn't have a label. Food is not something that should seem like a science experiment. Food it is already perfect as it is; it's a miracle. In the old days, we really would have appreciated this aspect of food being a miracle, as outside a global economy, crops and production can be victim to flood, famine, drought, infestation, weather of any kind and politics. We have been spoiled in expecting food to magically

Positive nutrition and strategic eating are your passport to your own fruitful health.

appear in our supermarkets. We have very little thought about the impact of this system on our producers (supermarkets driving hard bargains on price with farmers), or our environment (throwing out food and packaging), and how obtaining food from halfway across the globe impacts the nutrients in food.

Take the upgrades to get your health and vitality to such a place that you have personal resources to spare. This will change how you shop (shop local) and how you relate to your community and to your world. Don't let the planet die on our watch; really, it's up to us in our own small way through the choices we make).

Food eaten in its natural, fresh state gives us everything we need to live wonderful, fulfilling kick-ass lives. Nutritional science gives us vital knowledge, but using your instincts and your wisdom should not be dismissed either. You'll achieve a calm, dynamic energy, brain clarity and vibrant health. Don't ever accept that you can't do something to improve your health and your life, wherever you are on your journey.

Positive nutrition and strategic eating are your passport to your own fruitful health. Your choices impact our planet; never underestimate what can be achieved. If we all continue on this unconscious path, we will no longer have choices. So, take the upgrades, live a life well lived, laugh often, connect with friends, trust yourself and your choices, and make a difference by eating real food.

ABOUT THE AUTHOR

Kate Cook – corporate wellness expert, nutritional therapist, international speaker and author, and founder of The Nutrition Coach Clinic in Harley Street, London – has been delivering cutting-edge wellness programmes to some of the world's best-loved companies for nearly 20 years. Companies such as Time Warner, The Prudential, RBS, The Bank of England, and countless others have enjoyed soaking up Kate's food and health wisdom and reaping the benefits of optimum wellness for their employees. All with the dynamic energy, humour and enthusiasm that are the hallmarks of Kate's talks, seminars, and programmes.